D0830971

BETTER TO HAVE LOAFED AND LOST

The Best of
James Thurber

Biography

James Thurber (1894–1961) grew up in Columbus, Ohio, his early memories of which he hilariously relates in *My Life and Hard Times* (1933). After leaving college and a two-year sojourn in Paris he turned to journalism, finally landing a job with a struggling magazine called the *New Yorker*. He soon came to play a part in its success with his uniquely off-beat cartoons and writing. He continued to contribute to the magazine until his death and became justly world famous for his sophisticated humour, publishing nearly 30 books of fiction, cartoons, children's stories and essays. His timeless universal themes have seen his books translated into dozens of languages throughout the world.

BETTER TO HAVE LOAFED AND LOST

The Best of
James Thurber

EBURY
PRESS

First published in 2002 by Ebury Press

Better to Have Loafed and Lost
Arts and Texts copyright © 2002 by Rosemary A. Thurber

Anthology selection by Andrew Goodfellow

1 3 5 7 9 10 8 6 4 2

Ebury Press
Random House, 20 Vauxhall Bridge Road, London SW1V 2SA

Random House Australia (Pty) Limited
20 Alfred Street, Milsons Point, Sydney, New South Wales 2061, Australia

Random House New Zealand Limited
20 Poland Street, Glenfield, Auckland 10, New Zealand

Random House South Africa (Pty) Limited
Endulini, 5A Jubilee Road, Parktown 2193, South Africa

Random House UK Limited Reg. No. 954009

A CIP catalogue record for this book is available from the British Library

ISBN 0091885647
Jacket design by Jon Gray

Typeset in Chaparral Display by SX Composing DTP, Rayleigh, Essex
Printed and bound in Great Britain by
Mackays of Chatham plc, Chatham Kent

Papers used by Ebury Press are natural, recyclable products made from wood
grown in sustainable forests

Contents

Introduction

'My specialities,' Thurber once wrote, 'happen to be blood-hounds, holy matrimony, monsters and modern English usage.' It was the English usage, of which he was a fastidious critic, that drew him to Henry James, his favourite author. He loved emulating and parodying James, not just the rolling periods and the ponderousness, but the preciousness of those stories about writers, invariably called Vereker: 'Elliot Vereker was always coming into and going out of my life. He was the only man who ever continuously stimulated me to the brink of a nervous breakdown.'

On the face of it I suppose his admiration for a novelist as notoriously dense as Henry James is surprising, given how light Thurber himself feels, at least in retrospect. But then a reputation for lightness is the curse of any writer who is perceived as comic. 'I have most resented,' he said at a speech at the London launch of *A Thurber Carnival*, 'the application to what I write of such adjectives as "mild", "gentle", "pixie", and "zany". Having tried for four decades to make some social comment, it is something less than reassuring to discover that what a jittery America wants is a boppo laugh or nothing.'

Years before, in a contribution to Max Eastman's *Enjoyment of Laughter*, he argued that the best humour is that which 'lies closest to the familiar, to that part of the familiar which is humiliating, distressing, even tragic.' But few of us think of Thurber as a tragic writer.

I was dosed with Thurber early, at an age when other kids were still being palmed off with fairy stories. I have my mother to thank for that. She read him aloud to me, her shoulders shaking, tears rolling down her cheeks. She loved the bloodhound and holy matrimony Thurber best, the tales of ludicrous family disaster, dams breaking, beds falling, cars that wouldn't start. These seemed to be our stories, though we lived half a world away from Columbus, Ohio, and knew neither uncles struck down by the same disease that was killing the chestnut trees, nor aunties who lived in dread of electricity leaking out of the sockets. Such inventions were somehow wild and yet entirely familiar at the same time. This is the great joy of hyperbole in the hands of a master: it reminds us that we are all exaggerations.

At school my luck with Thurber held. We had an English teacher who could no more control his tears of laughter when reading him aloud to us than my mother could. His Thurber, though, was the more Jamesian one, the excoriator both of writing that was sloppily bad and too self-consciously good, the great juggler of the comedy of grammar and syntax – 'A certain type of person is wont to let "whether" get him down' – and the educated traveller though the minefields of foreign languages, one of which could sometimes be one's own. I still remember him swelling on the tide of that marvellous drama constructed from phrases from a Collins Pocket Interpreter, instructing the English how to speak French, though the fun lies in the accumulation of disasters of the sort only language guides ever adequately prepare you for.

> 'There has been an accident!' 'Go and fetch a policeman quickly.' 'Is there a doctor here?' 'Send for the ambulance.' 'He is seriously injured.' 'She has been run over.' 'He has been knocked down.' 'Someone has fallen in the water.' 'The ankle, the arm.' 'The back, a bone.' 'The face, the finger.' 'The foot, the head.' 'The knee, the leg.' 'The neck, the nose.' 'The wrist, the shoulder.'

And so on and so on, until the woes become too terrible to bear, the human frame too fragile to contemplate, and the farcical almost touches tragedy. OUR tragedy, since there is no one in particular lying there, coming apart in words, waiting for the ambulance and the interpreter, just us.

The Thurber I most liked at this age was the parodist and the bumbler. Families going to pieces when the car wouldn't start was one thing, but to be left alone in someone's house as in 'Nine Needles', and to go from spilling needles from the bathroom cabinet to wrecking the entire establishment as your attempts to make good the damage spiral into crazier and crazier acts of destruction – there was life as I recognized it, with all its excruciating embarrassments. Keep your Kafka, for me Thurber's vision of apocalyptic ineptitude was far more terrible.

Why Thurber's popularity waned for twenty or thirty years I am not sure. It might have had something to do with his cartoons, many of which dated quickly, and were too lettered for an illiterate age. It might have been his association with the *New Yorker* which for a long time seemed to have grown anodyne and private, not to say unfunny, clinging to the idea of WASP culture when other things were afoot. Or it might simply have been that we remembered Thurber too gently, whispering him out of the contemporary picture with those adjectives he so resented – mild, pixie, zany.

Reading him again now, what's particularly striking is how mild he wasn't. Have a look at 'What Are The Leftists Saying' if you want to rediscover what a steely critic of the intellectual temper of the times Thurber could be. Knockabout in shape – Thurber imagines taking a 'worker' to a meeting of leftists agitating in his name – the piece proceeds to investigate factionalism, dialectics, oversimplification and the 'unmasking' of ideology.

> Here I have brought the critic's sentence down to a definite meaning by providing a concrete instance. Leftist criticism does not believe in that, contending that all thought is in a state of motion, and that in every thought there exists simultaneously 'being', 'non-being', and 'becoming', and that in the end every thought disappears by being absorbed into its opposite. I am afraid that I am oversimplifying again.

The real revelations in this collection, though, are the stories of marital breakdown, the despair contingent on marital breakdown, one might say, to distinguish them from the more routine tales of domestic mishap. Sometimes Thurber's scenes from the sex war seem a little stuck in their own period: we can no longer accept as axiomatic that every wife is a harridan twice her husband's bulk, and that every husband is an ineffective mouse. It isn't that we refuse to believe that such proportions still exist, simply that every thought disappears by being absorbed into its opposite, and we think more today, when it comes to men and women, of causes and effects. But a story such as 'The Curb in the Sky', which tells of marriage to a woman who finishes one's sentences, transcends gender politics. It is fearful in its drollery, making much of what is on the surface very little, following an irritation until it descends into madness. Few writers can turn social comedy to horror as deftly as this – in an instant, even as we are still laughing, and on the point of a needle.

The blackest tale of all of this sort – for my money one of the blackest stories ever told – is 'The Whip-Poor-Will'. Starting with Kinstrey's insomnia, caused by the whip-poor-will's cry, 'rolling outs its loops and circles of sounds across the new day', taking us painfully through the stages of his mounting hopelessness, augmented by the failure of anyone in his household to understand his suffering – 'It's a notion,' says his wife. 'Don't let your nerves get the best of you. Use your willpower' – it climaxes in an ending so bloody I cannot bear to spoil your fun by alluding to it. All the descriptions of Kinstrey's torment are masterly. The whip-poor-will pecks at his perilous dreams like a vulture at a heart. When he looks at his sleeping wife, 'her arms straight and still outside the covers, her fingers relaxed', he wonders if she even has a subconscious, so automatically do her eyes close when she retires, and open when she wakes. 'The mechanism of her mind,' he marvels, 'was as simple as a cigarette box; it was either open or it was closed, and there was nothing else, nothing else, nothing else . . .'

Wherever they are stored, the personal habits of murderously unlovely people in literature – Karenin's cracking fingers, Rosamond Vincy's icy tap-water conversation – that cigarette box mind will be stored alongside them, the eyes opening and closing, and not a hint of a subconscious behind.

What raises a story like 'The Whip-Poor-Will' above the genre of the domestic-macabre is Thurber's seriousness. Don't let the mirth fool you: Thurber is writer who espies something dire in the familiar, and views it gravely. In 'Interview With a Lemming', there is a telling final exchange. 'I don't understand,' the scientist tells the lemming, 'why you lemmings all rush down to the sea and drown yourselves.' 'How curious,' replies the lemming, after noting the murderousness, maladjustedness, maleficence, malice, and muddled-headedness of the human race. 'The one thing I don't understand is why you human beings don't.'

Howard Jacobson

The Imperturbable Spirit

MR MONROE stood fingering some canes in a shop in the Fifties. Canes, it occurred to him, were imperturbable. He liked that adjective, which he had been encountering in a book he was reading on God, ethics, morals, humanism, and so on. The word stood staunch, like a bulwark, rumbled, like a caisson. Mr Monroe was pleased to find himself dealing in similes.

He finally decided not to buy a cane. Mrs Monroe was arriving that afternoon on the *Leviathan* and he would need both hands to wave porters around on the dock. His wife had to be looked after. She was such a child. When imperturbability was at the flood in Mr Monroe, his wife's nature took on for him a curiously dependent and childlike quality, not at all annoying, considerably endearing, and wholly mythical.

From the cane shop Mr Monroe wandered to a bookstore. On his imperturbable days it was almost impossible for him to work. He liked to brood and reflect and occasionally to catch glimpses of himself in store windows, slot-machine mirrors, etc., brooding and reflecting. He bought a paperback novel, in the original French, by André Maurois. The gesture – it was purely that for the simple reason that he did not read French – added a vague fillip to his day. Then he walked part way up Fifth Avenue, in the brisk air, and finally hailed a cab.

When he got home he took a bath, put on clean linen and another suit, and sank into a great chair to read some more in the book on God, morals, and so on. In the course of this he looked up three words in a dictionary, 'eschatological,' 'maleficent,' and 'teleology.' He read the definition of the last word twice, frowned, and let it go. Despite the fact that the outlook for mankind was far from bright in the particular chapter he was reading, Mr Monroe began to feel pretty much the master of his fate. Non-fiction, of a philosophical nature, always affected him that way, regardless of its content.

Mr Monroe wandered leisurely about the pier, complimenting himself on having remembered to get a customs pass, and on the way his mind kept dealing in interesting ideas. With an imperturbable frown, he watched the big liner nosing in.

Did fog at sea imply a malign aspect of the cosmos? If it came and went, without incident, did that connote luck, or what? Suppose it shielded an iceberg which sank the ship – did that prove the existence of an antic Malice? Mr Monroe liked the word antic. 'Antic,' he said, half aloud. He wondered vaguely if he, too, should not write a book about morals, malice, menace, and so on, showing how they could be handled by the imperturbable spirit. . . .

Little Mrs Monroe, burdened with coats and bundles, rosy, lovely, at length appeared. Mr Monroe's heart leapt up, but at the same time he set himself as if to receive a service in tennis. He remembered (oh, keenly) as he stepped toward her, how she was wont to regard him as a person likely to 'go to pieces' over trifles. Well, she would find him a changed man. He kissed her warmly, but withal in such a strangely masterful manner, that she was at first a little surprised – a tennis player taken aback by a sudden change in the tactics of an old, old opponent. In three minutes of backcourt rallying she figured out that he had been reading something, but she said nothing. She let his lobs go un-killed.

When Mrs Monroe stood in line at the desk where they assign inspectors, he offered to take her place. 'No, no,' she whispered. 'Just pretend you're not with me. It'll be easier.' A slow pallor came upon Mr Monroe's face.

'Whatta y' got?' he croaked.

'A dozen bottles of Benedictine,' she breathed.

'Oh my God!' said Mr Monroe, dropping, figuratively, his racquet.

An inspector stepped forward and stood waiting.

'So glad,' murmured Mrs Monroe to her husband, collectedly, as to a casual acquaintance. Mr Monroe fumbled at his hat, and wandered away, tugging at the left sleeve of his coat, a nervous gesture of his. She'd never get away with it. Twelve bottles! Quarts, probably, or magnums – no, it didn't come that way. Well, it came in big, bulky bottles anyway. Let's see, hadn't a new conspiracy law come in? Couldn't they send you to jail now? He could see himself in court, being flayed by a state's attorney. Mr Monroe had a phobia about law-breaking, even about ordinance-breaking. . . . 'Now, gentlemen of the jury . . .' The state's attorney put on his nose glasses, brought out a letter and read it in nasty, slow accents, a horrible, damning letter, which Mr Monroe had never seen before, but which, fiendishly enough, *was in his own handwriting*. The jury stirred.

'Now wait a minute –' began Mr Monroe, aloud.

'What *are* you talking about?' demanded his wife.

The courtroom mercifully faded. Mr Monroe turned and

stared at his wife. 'Ah – ha, dear!' he said, thickly. 'I'm all through!' she said, brightly. 'Let's go home.'

By the time they reached their house, Mr Monroe was his old self, or rather his new self, again. He had even pretty well persuaded himself that his iron nerve had got the Benedictine through the customs. His strange, masterful manner came back. No sooner had he got into his slippers, however, and reached for his book, than Mrs Monroe, in the next room, emitted a small squeak. 'My hatbox!' she cried. 'We left it at the dock!'

'Oh, damn! damn!' said Mr Monroe. 'Well, I'll have to go back after it, that's all. What was in it?'

'Some cute hats I got for almost nothing and – well, that's about all.'

'*About* all?'

'Well, three of the bottles.'

Mr Monroe squealed, in turn. 'Ah, God,' he said, bitterly.

'There's nothing to be afraid of now, silly,' his wife said. 'They were passed through!'

'I'm not afraid; I'll handle this,' murmured her husband.

In a sort of stupor he went out, hailed a cab, and climbed in. Life got you. A scheme of morals? A shield against menace? What good did that do? Impertur – ha! Menace got you – no bigger than a man's hand at first, no bigger than a hatbox. . . . 'Now, gentlemen of the jury . . . conspiracy . . . defraud the government . . . seditious . . .'

Mr Monroe crept whitely through the wide street entrance to the docks. The last stragglers were piling baggage into taxis in the noisy channel beyond. A few suitcases and boxes were still coming down the traveling platform from

'They were really porters, but Mr Monroe thought
they were guards'

the dock level above. At the bottom, where they tumbled in
a heap, two guards stood to receive them. They were really
porters, but Mr Monroe thought they were guards. They
had big jaws. One of them gradually turned into a state's
attorney before Mr Monroe's very eyes! The stricken
husband wandered idly over to the other side of the moving
platform. There stood a lonely, sinister hatbox, a trap, a
pitfall, Exhibit A. 'Now, gentlemen . . .'

'That your box, brother?' asked the state's attorney.

'Oh, no,' said Mr Monroe, 'nope.' The porter seemed disappointed. Mr Monroe walked out into the channel where the
taxis were. Then he walked back again; out again; and back
again. The guards had turned away and were fussing with a
trunk. Mr Monroe trembled. He walked stiffly to the hat-

box, picked it up, and walked stiffly through the doorway, out into the street.

'Hey!' cried a loud voice. Mr Monroe broke into a run. 'Taxi!' continued the loud voice. But Mr Monroe was a hundred yards away. He ran three blocks without stopping, walked half a block, and ran again. He came home by a devious route, rested a while outside his door, and went in. . . .

That night Mr Monroe read to his wife from the morals, ethics, and imperturbability book. He read in a deep, impressive voice, and slowly, for there was a lot his wife wouldn't grasp at once.

Mr Monroe Outwits a Bat

THE MONROES opened their summer place a little late, for carking cares had kept them long in town. The grass was greening and tangled when they arrived, and the house had a woodsy smell. Mr Monroe took a deep breath. 'I'll get a great sleep tonight,' he said. He put on some old clothes, pottered around, inspecting doors and windows, whistling. After dinner he went out under the stars and smelled the clear fine air. Abruptly there came to his ears a little scream from inside the house – the scream his wife gave when she dropped a cup or when some other trivial tragedy of the kitchen occurred. Mr Monroe hurried inside.

'Spider!' cried Mrs Monroe. 'Oh, kill it, kill it!' She always held that a spider, encountered but not slain, turned up in one's bed at night. Mr Monroe loved to kill spiders for his wife. He whacked this one off a tea towel with a newspaper, and scooped it outside the door into the petunia bed. It gave him a feeling of power, and enhanced the sweetness of his little wife's dependence on him. He was still glowing with his triumph, in a small, warm way, when he went to bed.

'Goodnight, dear,' he called, deeply. His voice was always a little deeper than usual, after a triumph.

'Goodnight, dear,' she called back from her room.

The night was sweet and clear. Nice old creaking sounds ran down the steps and back up again. Some of them sounded like the steps of a person.

'Afraid, dear?' he called out.

'Not with you here,' she answered, sleepily. There was a long, pleasant silence. Mr Monroe began to drowse. A very ominous sound brought him out of it, a distinct flut, a firm, insistent, rhythmic flut.

'Bat!' muttered Mr Monroe to himself.

At first he took the advent of the bat calmly. It seemed to be flying high, near the ceiling. He even boldly raised up on his elbows and peered through the dark. As he did so the bat, apparently out of sheer malice, almost clipped the top of his head. Mr Monroe scrambled under the covers, but instantly recovered his composure and put his head out

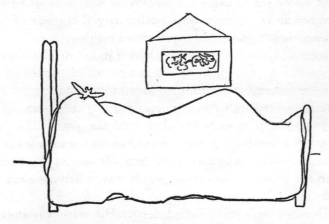

'Mr Monroe pulled the covers over his head'

again – just as the bat, returning in its orbit, skimmed across the bed once more. Mr Monroe pulled the covers over his head. It was the bat's round.

'Restless, dear?' called his wife, through her open door.

'What?' he said.

'Why, what's the matter?' she asked, slightly alarmed at his muffled tone.

'I'm all right, it's okay,' responded Mr Monroe, from under the covers.

'You sound funny,' said his wife. There was a pause.

'Goodnight, dear,' called Mr Monroe, poking his head out to say this, and pulling it in again.

'Goodnight.'

He strained his ears to hear through the covers, and found he could. The bat was still flitting above the bed in measured, relentless intervals. The notion came to the warm and stuffy Mr Monroe that the incessant repetition of a noise at regular intervals might drive a person crazy. He dismissed the thought, or tried to. If the dripping of water on a man's head, slowly, drip, drip, drip – flut, flut, flut . . .

'Damn it,' said Mr Monroe to himself. The bat was apparently just getting into its swing. It was flying faster. The first had just been practice. Mr Monroe suddenly bethought himself of a great spread of mosquito netting lying in a closet across the room. If he could get that and put it over the bed, he could sleep in peace. He poked his nose out from under a sheet, reached out a hand, and stealthily felt around for a match on a table by the bed – the light switch was yards away. Gradually his head and shoulders emerged. The bat seemed to be waiting for just this move. It zipped past his cheek. He flung himself back under the covers, with a great squeaking of springs.

'John?' called his wife.

'What's the matter now?' he asked, querulously.

'What *are* you doing?' she demanded.

'There's a bat in the room, if you want to know,' he said. 'And it keeps scraping the covers.'

'Scraping the covers?'

'Yes, scraping the covers.'

'It'll go away,' said his wife. 'They go away.'

'I'll drive it away!' shouted John Monroe, for his wife's tone was that of a mother addressing a child. 'How the devil the damn bat ever—' his voice grew dim because he was now pretty far under the bed clothes.

'I can't hear you, dear,' said Mrs Monroe. He popped his head out.

'I say how long is it before they go away?' he asked.

'It'll hang by its feet pretty soon and go to sleep,' said his wife, soothingly. 'It won't hurt you.' This last had a curious effect on Mr Monroe. Much to his own surprise he sat upright in bed, a little angry. The bat actually got him this time, brushed his hair, with a little 'Squeep!'

'Hey!' yelled Mr Monroe.

'What *is* it, dear?' called his wife. He leaped out of bed, now completely panic-stricken, and ran for his wife's room. He went in and closed the door behind him, and stood there.

'Get in with me, dear,' said Mrs Monroe.

'I'm all right,' he retorted, irritably. 'I simply want to get something to rout that thing with. I couldn't find anything in my room.' He flicked on the lights.

'There's no sense in your getting all worn out fighting a bat,' said his wife. 'They're terribly quick.' There seemed to him to be an amused sparkle in her eyes.

'Well, I'm terribly quick too,' grumbled Mr Monroe, trying to keep from shivering, and he slowly folded a newspaper into a sort of club. With this in his hand he stepped to the door. 'I'll shut your door after me,' he said, 'so the bat won't get in your room.' He went out, firmly closing the door behind him. He crept slowly along the hall till he came to his own room. He waited a while and listened. The bat was still going strong. Mr Monroe lifted the paper club and struck the jamb of the door, from the outside, a terrific blow. 'Wham!' went the blow. He hit again. 'Wham!'

'Did you get it, dear?' called his wife, her voice coming dimly through her door.

'Okay,' cried her husband, 'I got it.' He waited a long while. Then he slipped, on tiptoe, to a couch in the corridor halfway between his room and his wife's and gently, ever so gently, let himself down upon it. He slept lightly, because he was pretty chilly, until dawn, got up and tiptoed to his room. He peered in. The bat was gone. Mr Monroe got into bed and went to sleep.

Mr Monroe and the Moving Men

MR MONROE had never really had any experience in moving household goods before he did it, single-handed, on the eighth of August, 1930. The date will always be fixed in his mind that way, formally, formidably. It was rather an unusual time to move, but it couldn't be helped because on the ninth of August wreckers were going to start tearing down the house. Little Mrs Monroe was away, unavoidably away, terrifyingly away. We have here, then, the makings of a character study – or would have except for the fact that Mr Monroe didn't really have any character. He had a certain charm, yes; but not character. He evaded difficult situations; he had no talent for firm resolution; he immolated badly; and he wasn't even very good at renunciation, except when he was tired or a little sick. Not, you will see, the man to move household goods into storage when his wife is away.

The packers and movers were to come at two o'clock. Mrs Monroe could have told her husband that they wouldn't arrive until four-thirty; or he would have known it himself if always before, when they moved, he had not sneaked away from the house. Always before, Mr Monroe had been just as surprised to find himself in a new place as a mother dog is when she is lifted out from among the shoes in the clothes closet, where she has decided to have her puppies, and put into a lovely airy box with a pink coverlet.

Before she went away, little Mrs Monroe had led her husband from room to room, pointing out what was to go into storage and what was to be sent to the summer place in Connecticut. It was all quite simple, she told him. Apparently John Monroe hadn't been listening, however, for now, as he walked restlessly from room to room, picking up vases and putting them down again, he found he wasn't sure about anything. He wasn't sure about the china and glassware, for one thing. He stood and stared at them, trying to remember what it was his wife had said. All that he could recall was that she had spoken in the slow, precise way in which she always spoke to him in a crisis, as if he were a little deaf or feeble-minded. He decided, finally, that the glassware and china went into storage. Then he decided that they didn't. He tried to remember whether they already had plates and glasses at the summer place and realized, of course, that they must have. They ate there; they lived there. But he also realized that the ways of women are beyond the simple understanding of the masculine mind, and that the fact that a wife already has one set of dishes and glasses is no reason she can't – nay, mustn't, maybe – have another set. Mr Monroe sighed, and went in and turned on the bath water; then he turned it off again, for there were no towels. By this time it was getting on toward three o'clock. He took to wandering aimlessly around, wondering if he should wrap something up, or what.

Mr Monroe and the Moving Men

After a time he came to a halt in front of a large chair – a large, flowered chair, he would have described it to his wife over the phone – which, in her tour around the place with him, little Mrs Monroe, he felt positive, had said something very definite about. He wondered what it had been. It now occurred to him, after deep thought, that his wife must have spoken only about the things which were to be saved out of storage – it would have been silly for her to point out things that were to go to the warehouse because nine-tenths of the things were to go to the warehouse. Obviously, then, reasoned Mr Monroe – and he was a bit proud of his brilliance in this matter – obviously she had pointed out only the things that were to be kept out. Now if he could only remember which things she had pointed out, he would be safe. He decided to move away from the flowered chair, to let it go, for the longer he looked at it the stronger became his conviction that he had never seen it before in his life. This took him back to the chinaware and glasses. She must have said: 'And this, John. Remember – all this goes to the summer place.' Certainly. Or maybe she had said: 'And watch them when they pack this for storage, John; don't let them break anything.' Hmm. Mr Monroe lighted a cigarette and sat down. It was now almost four o'clock. Suppose the moving men didn't come? Well, if they didn't, the wreckers would tear the place down next day, with the furniture in it. Maybe he could prevail on the wreckers, for some enormous sum, to pack and move the stuff out, before they started wrecking. Of course wreckers wouldn't want to do that, but he saw himself dominating them, when they demurred. 'See here, my men,' he heard

15

himself saying, coldly, '*I'm* in charge here – get that!' He loved himself in that role, and was often in it, in his day dreams, which, on this occasion, were abruptly interrupted by the arrival of the packers and movers.

They set to work so fast that three tables and a bed were down the stairs and onto the sidewalk before Mr Monroe could say anything. Well, he was pretty sure about the great big pieces of furniture, anyway – they must go to storage. Great big pieces of furniture were always stored – that's why storage warehouses were so big. Mr Monroe began to feel that he was getting a grip on the situation. 'What about the china, chief?' one of the men asked him. Mr Monroe hesitated. 'Pack it and let it stand a while,' he said, at last. 'I

'They set to work so fast that three tables and a bed were down the stairs before Mr Monroe could say anything'

want to think about it.' From downstairs later he could hear the voices of the men, huge, sweating, rough fellows, joking about him: 'This guy wants to think it over – ja get that, Joe?' Mr Monroe's indecision and evident nervousness began to show up in the movers' attitude toward him. 'The 'chief' and 'mister' with which they had first addressed him changed to 'buddy' and 'pardner' and finally, as Mr Monroe strove desperately for an air of dignity and authority, to 'sonny.'

In the end, most of the decisions were made by the men themselves. Joe stood with one of his hairy paws on a small writing desk. 'How about this, scout?' he asked. It was a favorite piece of Mrs Monroe's; John couldn't remember whether she had said anything about it; 'Okay,' said Joe, and he moved it out. John hadn't said anything. So it went.

'The packers got the chinaware and glasses into two barrels'

Meanwhile two packers had got the chinaware and glasses into two barrels. 'What about it, buddy?' they finally asked the head of the house. 'Well, here's the way it is,' he began. 'You see, it's quite a problem. I—' 'Better store it, sonny,' said one of the men. 'You don't need all this china.' 'Does it look like summer china to you?' asked Mr Monroe, rather meekly. 'Naw, dat's winter china,' said a man named Mike. 'Take it away, Bill.' Bill took it away, out to the storage van. Mr Monroe was now certain that his wife had wanted it saved out for the summer house. 'Oh God, God,' he said to himself, walking around and smoking rapidly.

By the time the movers reached the kitchen utensils, and called them to Mr Monroe's attention, he was becoming overwhelmed by the idiotic conviction that he was in the wrong house. What the hell were kitchen utensils doing here? They were up at the summer place, weren't they? It was only after an agonizing few moments that he realized they had rented the summer house furnished. The men, tired of waiting for directions, picked the kitchenware up and carted it out to the van. 'Okay,' murmured Mr Monroe.

At length, there was nothing left but a few odds and ends, one of which was a large tin receptacle marked 'Flour.' 'Can't store this, buddy,' one of the men said, showing the head of the house that the can was two-thirds full of flour, with a spoon in it. Mr Monroe took the can, and when none of the men was looking, shoved the thing into a closet, shut the door, and sighed. 'Everything out of dat closet?' asked Joe, appearing from somewhere. 'Okay,' said Mr Monroe. 'Okay,' said Joe. The men went away as quickly as they had come.

MR MONROE AND THE MOVING MEN

Mr Monroe sank into a chair, one of the three or four objects he had saved out for the summer house. He slowly began to convince himself that all of his decisions – or the men's, anyway – had been right. After all, they were men experienced in moving. He began to feel pretty good about the whole thing; it was over and done with, thank God. Just then, into the edge of his consciousness, stalked a tall, thin thought. Mrs Monroe had told him what to do about getting stuff to the summer house: a certain transfer man, who delivered out of town, was to call; John had been given his name, his address, and his phone number. Mr Monroe crushed a cigarette in his hand. Then he cried aloud. He couldn't remember the man's name. He couldn't remember anything.

Mr Monroe Holds the Fort

THE COUNTRY house, on this particular wintry afternoon, was most enjoyable. Night was trudging up the hill and the air was sharp. Mr Monroe had already called attention several times to the stark beauty of the black tree branches limned, as he put it, against the sky. The wood fire had settled down to sleepy glowing in the grate.

'It *is* a little lonely, though,' said Mrs Monroe. (The nearest house was far away.)

'I love it,' said her husband, darkly. At moments and in places like this, he enjoyed giving the impression of a strong, silent man wrapped in meditation. He stared, brooding, into the fire. Mrs Monroe, looking quite tiny and helpless, sat on the floor at his feet and leaned against him. He gave her shoulder two slow, reflective pats.

'I really don't mind staying here when Germaine is here – just we two,' said Mrs Monroe, 'but I think I would be terrified if I were alone.' Germaine, the maid, a buxom, fearless woman, was in town on shopping leave. The Monroes had thought it would be fun to spend the weekend alone and get their own meals, the way they used to.

'There's nothing in the world to be afraid of,' said Mrs Monroe.

'Oh, it gets so terribly black outside, and you hear all kinds of funny noises at night that you don't hear during the day.' Mr Monroe explained to her why that was – expansion (said he) of woodwork in the cold night air, and so on. From there he somehow went into a discussion of firearms, which would have betrayed to practically anyone that his knowledge of guns was limited to a few impressive names like Colt and Luger. They were one of those things he was always going to read up on but never did. He mentioned quietly, however, that he was an excellent shot.

'Mr Farrington left his pistol here, you know,' said Mrs Monroe, 'but I've never touched it – ugh!'

'He did?' cried her husband. 'Where is it? I'd like to take a look at it.' Mr Farrington was the man from whom they had taken, on long lease, the Connecticut place.

'It's upstairs in the chest of drawers in the back room,' said Mrs Monroe. Her husband, despite her protests, went up and got it and brought it down. 'Please put it away!' said his wife. 'Is it loaded? Oh, don't do that! Please!' Mr Monroe, looking grim and competent, was aiming the thing, turning it over, scowling at it.

'It's loaded all right,' he said, 'all five barrels.'

'Chambers,' said his wife.

'Yes,' he said. 'Let me show you how to use it – after all, you can never tell when you're going to need a gun.'

'Oh, I'd never use it – even if one of those convicts that escaped yesterday came right up the stairs and I could shoot him, I'd just stand there. I'd be *paralyzed*!'

'Nonsense!' said Mr Monroe. 'You don't have to shoot a

'Burglars flitting about in the attic of a house in which
the master is home alone'

man. Get the drop on him, stand him up with his face
against a wall, and phone the police. Look here—' he
covered an imaginary figure, backed him against the wall,
and sat down at the phone table. 'Always keep your eye on
him; don't look into the transmitter.' Mr Monroe glared at
his man, lifted up the receiver, holding the hook down with
his finger, and spoke quietly to the phone. In the midst of
this the phone rang. Mr Monroe started sharply.

'It's for you, dear,' he said presently. His wife took the
receiver.

How curiously things happen! That is what Mr Monroe
thought, an hour later, as he drove back from the station
after taking his wife there to catch the 7.10. Imagine her

mother getting one of those fool spells at this time! Imagine expecting a grown daughter to come running every time you felt a little dizzy! Imagine – well, the ways of women were beyond him. He turned into the drive of the country house. Judas, but it was dark! Dark and silent. Mr Monroe didn't put the machine in the garage. He got out and stood still, listening. Off toward the woods somewhere he heard a thumping noise. Partridge drumming, thought Mr Monroe. But partridge didn't thump, they whirred – didn't they? Oh, well, they probably thumped at this time of year.

It was good to get inside the house. He built up the fire, and turned on the overhead lights – his wife never allowed them turned on. Then he went into a couple of other rooms and turned on more lights. He wished he had gone in town with her. Of course she'd be back in the morning on the 10.10 and they'd have the rest of that day – Sunday – together. Still . . . he went to the drawer where he had put the revolver and got it out. He fell to wondering whether the thing would work. Long-unused guns often jammed, or exploded. He went out into the kitchen, carrying the pistol. His wife had told him to be sure and get himself a snack. He opened the refrigerator door, looked in, decided he wasn't hungry, and closed it again. He went back to the living-room and began to pace up and down. He decided to put the pistol on the mantel, butt toward him. Then he practiced making quick grabs for it. Presently he sat down in a chair, picked up a *Nation* and began to read, at random: 'Two men are intimately connected with the killing of striking workers at Marion, North Carolina. . . .' Where had those convicts his wife mentioned escaped from? Dannemora? Matteawan? How far were those places from this house? Maybe having all the lights on was a bad idea? He got up and turned the upper lights off; and then turned them on again. . . . There was a step outside. Crunch! Crunch! . . . Mr Monroe hurried to the mantel, knocked the gun on to the floor, fumbled for it, and stuck it in a hip pocket just as a knock sounded at the door.

'Wha—' began Mr Monroe, and was surprised to find he couldn't say anything else. The knocking continued. He stepped to the door, stood far to one side, and said, 'Yeh?' A cheery voice responded. Reassured, Mr Monroe opened the door. A motorist wanted to know how to get to the Wilton road. Mr Monroe told him, speaking quite loudly. Afterwards, lifted up by this human contact, he went back to his reading in the *Nation*: 'Around 1.30 a.m. one of the foremen approached young Luther Bryson, 22, one of the victims, and harangued him: "If you strike this time, you—, we will shoot it out with you." . . .' Mr Monroe put the magazine down. He got up and went to the victrola, selected a jazz record, and began to play it. It occurred to him that if there were steps outside, he couldn't hear them. He shut the machine off. The abrupt silence made him stand still, listening. He heard all kinds of noises. One of them came from upstairs – a quick, sliding noise, like a convict slipping into a clothes closet . . . the fellow had a beard and a blue-steel gun . . . a man in the dark had the advantage. Mr Monroe's mouth began to feel stuffy. 'Damn it! This can't go on!' he said aloud, and felt bucked up. Then someone put his heel down sharply on the floor just above. Mr Monroe tentatively picked up a flashlight, and pulled the pistol from his pocket. The phone rang sharply. 'Good God!' said Mr Monroe, backing against a wall. He slid on to the chair in front of the phone, with the gun in his right hand, and took up the receiver with his left. When he spoke into the transmitter his eyes kept roving around the room. 'H'lo,' he said. It was Mrs Monroe. Her mother was all right. Was he all right? He was fine. What was he doing? Oh, reading. (He kept the gun trained on the foot of the steps leading upstairs.) Well, what would he think if she came back out on the midnight train? Her mother was all right. Would he be too sleepy to wait up and meet her? Hell, no! That was fine! Do that! . . .

Mr Monroe hung up the receiver with a profound sigh of relief. He looked at his watch. Hm, wouldn't have to leave for the station for nearly two hours. Whistling, he went out to the refrigerator (still carrying the gun) and fetched out the butter and some cold meat. He made a couple of sandwiches (laying the gun on the kitchen table) and took them into the living-room (putting the gun in his pocket). He turned off the overhead lights, sat down, picked up a *Harper's* and began to read. Abruptly, that flitting, clothes-closety sound came from upstairs again. Mr Monroe finished his sandwiches hurriedly, with the gun on his lap, got up, went from room to room turning off the extra lights, put on his hat and overcoat, locked several doors, went out and got into his car. After all, he could read just as well at the station, and he would be sure of being there on time – might fall asleep otherwise. He started the engine, and whirled out of the drive. He felt for the pistol, which was in his overcoat pocket. He would slip it back into the chest of drawers upstairs later on. Mr Monroe came to a crossroads and a light. He began to whistle.

The Car We Had to Push

MANY AUTOBIOGRAPHERS, among them Lincoln Steffens and Gertrude Atherton, described earthquakes their families have been in. I am unable to do this because my family was never in an earthquake, but we went through a number of things in Columbus that were a great deal like earthquakes. I remember in particular some of the repercussions of an old Reo we had that wouldn't go unless you pushed it for quite a way and suddenly let your clutch out. Once, we had been able to start the engine easily by cranking it, but we had had the car for so many years that finally it wouldn't go unless you pushed it and let your clutch out. Of course, it took more than one person to do this; it took sometimes as many as five or six, depending on the grade of the roadway and conditions underfoot. The car was unusual in that the clutch and brake were on the same pedal, making it quite easy to stall the engine after it got started, so that the car would have to be pushed again.

My father used to get sick at his stomach pushing the car, and very often was unable to go to work. He had never liked the machine, even when it was good, sharing my ignorance and suspicion of all automobiles of twenty years ago and longer. The boys I went to school with used to be able to

27

'It took sometimes as many as five or six'

identify every car as it passed by: Thomas Flyer, Firestone-Columbus, Stevens Duryea, Rambler, Winton, White Steamer, etc. I never could. The only car I was really interested in was one that the Get-Ready Man, as we called him, rode around town in: a big Red Devil with a door in the back. The Get-Ready Man was a lank unkempt elderly gentleman with wild eyes and a deep voice who used to go about shouting at people through a megaphone to prepare for the end of the world. 'GET READY! GET READY-Y!' he would bellow. 'THE WORLLLD IS COMING TO AN END!' His startling exhortations would come up, like summer thunder, at the most unexpected times and in the most surprising places. I remember once during Mantell's production of 'King Lear' at the Colonial Theater, that the Get-Ready Man added his bawlings to the squealing of Edgar and the ranting of the King and the mouthing of the Fool, rising from somewhere in the balcony to join in. The theater was in absolute darkness and there were rumblings of thunder and flashes of lightning offstage. Neither father nor I, who were there, ever completely got over the scene, which went something like this:

Edgar: Tom's a-cold.—O, do de, do de, do de!—Bless thee from whirlwinds, star-blasting, and taking . . . the foul fiend vexes!

(Thunder off.

Lear: What! Have his daughters brought him to this pass?—

Get-Ready Man: Get ready! Get ready!
Edgar: Pillicock sat on Pillicock-Hill:—

Halloo, halloo, loo, loo!

(Lightning flashes.

Get-Ready Man: The Worllld is com-ing to an End!
Fool: This cold night will turn us all to fools and madmen!

'The Get-Ready Man'

Edgar: Take heed o' the foul fiend: obey thy paren——

Get-Ready Man: Get *Rea*-dy!

Edgar: Tom's a-*cold*!

Get-Ready Man: The *Worr*-uld is coming to an end! . . .

They found him finally, and ejected him, still shouting. The Theater, in our time, has known few such moments.

But to get back to the automobile. One of my happiest memories of it was when, in its eighth year, my brother Roy got together a great many articles from the kitchen, placed them in a square of canvas, and swung this under the car with a string attached to it so that, at a twitch, the canvas would give way and the steel and tin things would clatter to the street. This was a little scheme of Roy's to frighten father, who had always expected the car might explode. It worked perfectly. That was twenty-five years ago, but it is one of the few things in my life I would like to live over again if I could. I don't suppose that I can, now. Roy twitched the string in the middle of a lovely afternoon, on Brydon Road near Eighteenth Street. Father had closed his eyes and, with his hat off, was enjoying a cool breeze. The clatter on the asphalt was tremendously effective: knives, forks, can-openers, pie pans, pot lids, biscuit-cutters, ladles, egg-beaters fell, beautifully together, in a lingering, clamant crash. 'Stop the *car*!' shouted father. 'I can't,' Roy said. 'The engine fell out.' 'God Almighty!' said father, who knew what *that* meant, or knew what it sounded as if it might mean.

It ended unhappily of course, because we finally had to drive back and pick up the stuff and even father knew the difference between the works of an automobile and the equipment of a pantry. My mother wouldn't have known, however, nor *her* mother. My mother, for instance, thought – or, rather, knew – that it was dangerous to drive an automobile without gasoline: it fried the valves, or something. 'Now don't you dare drive all over town without gasoline!' she would say to us when we started off. Gasoline, oil, and water were much the same to her, a fact that made her life both confusing and perilous. Her greatest dread, however, was the victrola – we had a very early one, back in the 'Come Josephine in My Flying Machine' days. She had an idea that the victrola might blow up. It alarmed her, rather than reassured her, to explain that the phonograph was run neither by gasoline nor by electricity. She could only suppose that it was propelled by some newfangled and untested apparatus which was likely to let go at any minute, making us all the victims and martyrs of the wild-eyed Edison's dangerous experiments. The telephone she was comparatively at peace with, except, of course, during storms, when for some reason or other she always took the receiver off the hook and let it hang. She came naturally by her confused and groundless fears, for her own mother lived the latter years of her life in the horrible suspicion that electricity was dripping invisibly all over the house. It leaked, she contended, out of empty sockets if the wall switch had been left on. She would go around screwing in bulbs, and if they lighted up she would hastily and fearfully turn off the wall switch and go back to her *Pearson's* or *Everybody's*, happy in the satisfaction that she had stopped not only a costly but a dangerous leakage. Nothing could ever clear this up for her.

Our poor old Reo came to a horrible end, finally. We had

'Electricity was leaking all over the house'

parked it too far from the curb on a street with a car line. It was late at night and the street was dark. The first streetcar that came along couldn't get by. It picked up the tired old automobile as a terrier might seize a rabbit and drubbed it unmercifully, losing its hold now and then but catching a new grip a second later. Tires booped and whooshed, the fenders queeled and graked, the steering-wheel rose up like a specter and disappeared in the direction of Franklin Avenue with a melancholy whistling sound, bolts and gadgets flew like sparks from a Catherine wheel. It was a splendid spectacle but, of course, saddening to everybody (except the motorman of the streetcar, who was sore). I think some of us broke down and wept. It must have been the weeping that caused grandfather to take on so terribly. Time was all mixed up in his mind; automobiles and the like he never remembered having seen. He apparently gathered, from the talk and excitement and weeping, that somebody had died. Nor did he let go of this delusion. He insisted, in fact, after almost a week in which we strove mightily to divert him, that it was a sin and a shame and a disgrace on the family to put the funeral off any longer. 'Nobody is dead! The automobile is smashed!' shouted my father, trying for the thirtieth time to explain the situation to the old man. 'Was he drunk?' demanded grandfather, sternly. 'Was who drunk?' asked father. 'Zenas,' said grandfather. He had a name for the corpse now: it was his brother Zenas, who, as it happened, *was* dead, but not from driving an automobile while intoxicated. Zenas had died in 1866. A sensitive, rather poetical boy of twenty-one when the Civil War broke out, Zenas had gone to South America – 'just,' as he wrote back, 'until it blows over.' Returning after the war had blown over, he caught the same disease that was killing off the chestnut trees in those years, and passed away. It was the only case in history where a tree doctor had to be called in to spray a person, and our family had felt it very keenly; nobody else in the United States caught the blight. Some of us have looked upon Zenas' fate as a kind of poetic justice.

Now that grandfather knew, so to speak, who was dead, it became increasingly awkward to go on living in the same house with him as if nothing had happened. He would go into towering rages in which he threatened to write to the

'He caught the same disease that was killing
the chestnut trees'

Board of Health unless the funeral were held at once. We realized that something had to be done. Eventually, we persuaded a friend of father's, named George Martin, to dress up in the manner and costume of the eighteen-sixties and pretend to be Uncle Zenas, in order to set grandfather's mind at rest. The impostor looked fine and impressive in sideburns and a high beaver hat, and not unlike the daguerreotypes of Zenas in our album. I shall never forget the night, just after dinner, when this Zenas walked into the living-room. Grandfather was stomping up and down, tall, hawk-nosed, round-oathed. The newcomer held out both his hands. 'Clem!' he cried to grandfather. Grandfather turned slowly, looked at the intruder, and snorted. 'Who air *you*?' he demanded in his deep, resonant voice. 'I'm Zenas!' cried Martin. 'Your brother Zenas, fit as a fiddle and sound as a dollar!' 'Zenas, my foot!' said grandfather. 'Zenas died of the chestnut blight in '66!'

Grandfather was given to these sudden, unexpected, and extremely lucid moments; they were generally more embarrassing than his other moments. He comprehended before he went to bed that night that the old automobile had been destroyed and that its destruction had caused all the turmoil in the house. 'It flew all to pieces, Pa,' my mother told him, in graphically describing the accident. 'I knew 'twould,' growled grandfather. 'I allus told ye to git a Pope-Toledo.'

The Day the Dam Broke

MY MEMORIES of what my family and I went through during the 1913 flood in Ohio I would gladly forget. And yet neither the hardships we endured nor the turmoil and confusion we experienced can alter my feeling toward my native state and city. I am having a fine time now and wish Columbus were here, but if anyone ever wished a city was in hell it was during that frightful and perilous afternoon in 1913 when the dam broke, or, to be more exact, when everybody in town thought that the dam broke. We were both ennobled and demoralized by the experience. Grandfather especially rose to magnificent heights which can never lose their splendor for me, even though his reactions to the flood were based upon a profound misconception; namely, that Nathan Bedford Forrest's cavalry was the menace we were called upon to face. The only possible means of escape for us was to flee the house, a step which grandfather sternly forbade, brandishing his old army sabre in his hand. 'Let the sons ——— come!' he roared. Meanwhile hundreds of people were streaming by our house in wild panic, screaming 'Go east! Go east!' We had to stun grandfather with the ironing board. Impeded as we were by the inert form of the old gentleman – he was taller than six feet and weighed almost a hundred and seventy pounds – we were passed, in the first half-mile, by practically everybody else in the city. Had grandfather not come to, at the corner of Parsons Avenue and Town Street, we would unquestionably have been overtaken and engulfed by the roaring waters – that is, if there had *been* any roaring waters. Later, when the panic had died down and people had gone rather sheepishly back to their homes and their offices, minimizing the distances they had run and offering various reasons for running, city engineers pointed out that even if the dam had broken, the water level would not have risen more than two additional inches in the West Side. The West Side was, at the time of the dam scare, under thirty feet of water – as, indeed, were all Ohio river towns during the great spring floods of twenty years ago. The East Side (where we lived and where all the running occurred) had never been in any danger at all. Only a rise of some ninety-five feet could have caused the flood waters to flow over High Street – the thoroughfare that divided the east side of town from the west – and engulf the East Side.

The fact that we were all as safe as kittens under a cookstove did not, however, assuage in the least the fine despair and the grotesque desperation which seized upon the residents of the East Side when the cry spread like a grass fire that the dam had given way. Some of the most dignified, staid, cynical, and clear-thinking men in town abandoned their wives, stenographers, homes, and offices and ran east. There are few alarms in the world more terrifying than 'The dam has broken!' There are few persons capable of stopping to reason when that clarion cry strikes upon their ears, even persons who live in towns no nearer than five hundred miles to a dam.

The Columbus, Ohio, broken-dam rumor began, as I recall it, about noon of March 12, 1913. High Street, the main canyon of trade, was loud with the placid hum of business and the buzzing of placid businessmen arguing, computing, wheedling, offering, refusing, compromising. Darius Conningway, one of the foremost corporation lawyers in the Middle-West, was telling the Public Utilities Commission in the language of Julius Caesar that they might as well try to move the Northern star as to move him. Other men were making their little boasts and their little

'Two thousand people were in full flight'

gestures. Suddenly somebody began to run. It may be that he had simply remembered, all of a moment, an engagement to meet his wife, for which he was now frightfully late. Whatever it was, he ran east on Broad Street (probably toward the Maramor Restaurant, a favorite place for a man to meet his wife). Somebody else began to run, perhaps a newsboy in high spirits. Another man, a portly gentleman of affairs, broke into a trot. Inside of ten minutes, everybody on High Street, from the Union Depot to the Courthouse was running. A loud mumble gradually crystallized into the dread word 'dam.' 'The dam has broke!' The fear was put into words by a little old lady in an electric, or by a traffic cop, or by a small boy: nobody knows who, nor does it now really matter. Two thousand people were abruptly in full flight. 'Go east!' was the cry that arose – east away from the river, east to safety. 'Go east! Go east! Go east!'

Black streams of people flowed eastward down all the streets leading in that direction; these streams, whose headwaters were in the drygoods stores, office buildings, harness shops, movie theaters, were fed by trickles of housewives, children, cripples, servants, dogs, and carts, slipping out of the houses past which the main streams flowed, shouting and screaming. People ran out leaving fires burning and food cooking and doors wide open. I remember, however, that my mother turned out all the fires and that she took with her a dozen eggs and two loaves of bread. It was her plan to make Memorial Hall, just two blocks away, and take refuge somewhere in the top of it, in one of the dusty rooms where war veterans met and where old battle flags and stage scenery were stored. But the seething throngs, shouting 'Go east!' drew her along and the rest of us with her. When grandfather regained full consciousness, at Parsons Avenue, he turned upon the retreating mob like a vengeful prophet and exhorted the men to form ranks and stand off the Rebel dogs, but at length he, too, got the idea that the dam had broken and, roaring 'Go east!' in his powerful voice, he caught up in one arm a small child and in the other a slight clerkish man of perhaps forty-two and we slowly began to gain on those ahead of us.

A scattering of fireman, policemen, and army officers in dress uniforms – there had been a review at Fort Hayes, in the northern part of town – added color to the surging billows of people. 'Go east!' cried a little child in a piping voice, as she ran past a porch on which drowsed a lieutenant-colonel of infantry. Used to quick decisions, trained to immediate obedience, the officer bounded off the porch and, running at full tilt, soon passed the child, bawling 'Go east!' The two of them emptied rapidly the houses of the little street they were on. 'What is it? What is it?' demanded a fat, waddling man who intercepted the colonel. The officer dropped behind and asked the little child what it was. 'The dam has broke!' gasped the girl. 'The dam has broke!' roared the colonel. 'Go east! Go east! Go east!' He was soon leading, with the exhausted child in his arms, a fleeing company of three hundred persons who had gathered around him from living-rooms, shops, garages, backyards, and basements.

Nobody has ever been able to compute with any exactness how many people took part in the great rout of 1913, for the panic, which extended from the Winslow Bottling Works in the south end to Clintonville, six miles north, ended as abruptly as it began and the bobtail and ragtag and velvet-gowned groups of refugees melted away and slunk home, leaving the streets peaceful and deserted. The shouting, weeping, tangled evacuation of the city lasted not more than two hours in all. Some few people got as far east as Reynoldsburg, twelve miles away; fifty or more reached the Country Club, eight miles away; most of the others gave up, exhausted, or climbed trees in Franklin Park, four miles out. Order was restored and fear dispelled finally by means of militiamen riding about in motor lorries bawling through megaphones: 'The dam has *not* broken!' At first this tended only to add to the confusion and increase the panic, for many stampeders thought the soldiers were bellowing 'The dam has now broken!' thus setting an official seal of authentication on the calamity.

All the time, the sun shone quietly and there was nowhere any sign of oncoming waters. A visitor in an airplane, looking down on the straggling, agitated masses of people below, would have been hard put to it to divine a reason for the phenomenon. It must have inspired, in such an observer, a peculiar kind of terror, like the sight of the *Marie Celeste*, abandoned at sea, its galley fires peacefully burning, its tranquil decks bright in the sunlight.

An aunt of mine, Aunt Edith Taylor, was in a movie theater on High Street when, over and above the sound of the piano in the pit (a W. S. Hart picture was being shown), there rose the steadily increasing tromp of running feet. Persistent shouts rose above the tromping. An elderly man, sitting near my aunt, mumbled something, got out of his seat, and went up the aisle at a dogtrot. This started everybody. In an instant the audience was jamming the aisles. 'Fire!' shouted a woman who always expected to be burned up in a theater; but now the shouts outside were louder and coherent. 'The dam has broke!' cried somebody. 'Go east!' screamed a small woman in front of my aunt. And east they went, pushing and shoving and clawing, knocking women and children down, emerging finally into the street, torn and sprawling. Inside the theater, Bill Hart was calmly calling some desperado's bluff and the brave girl at the piano played 'Row! Row! Row!' loudly and then 'In My Harem.' Outside, men were streaming across the Statehouse yard, others were climbing trees, a woman managed to get up onto the 'These Are My Jewels' statue, whose bronze figures of Sherman, Stanton, Grant, and Sheridan watched with cold unconcern the going to pieces of the capital city.

'I ran south to State Street, east on State to Third, south on Third to Town, and out east on Town,' my Aunt Edith has written me. 'A tall spare woman with grim eyes and a determined chin ran past me down the middle of the street. I was still uncertain as to what was the matter, in spite of all the shouting. I drew up alongside the woman with some effort, for although she was in her late fifties, she had a beautiful easy running form and seemed to be in excellent condition. "What is it?" I puffed. She gave me a quick glance and then looked ahead again, stepping up her pace a trifle. "Don't ask me, ask God!" she said.

'When I reached Grant Avenue, I was so spent that Dr H. R. Mallory – you remember Dr Mallory, the man with the

"'It's got us!' he shouted'

white beard who looks like Robert Browning? – well, Dr Mallory, whom I had drawn away from at the corner of Fifth and Town, passed me. "It's got us!" he shouted, and I felt sure that whatever it was *did* have us, for you know what conviction Dr Mallory's statements always carried. I didn't know at the time what he meant, but I found out later. There was a boy behind him on roller-skates, and Dr Mallory mistook the swishing of the skates for the sound of rushing water. He eventually reached the Columbus School for Girls, at the corner of Parsons Avenue and Town Street, where he collapsed, expecting the cold frothing waters of the Scioto to sweep him into oblivion. The boy on the skates swirled past him and Dr Mallory realized for the first time what he had been running from. Looking back up the street, he could see no signs of water, but nevertheless, after resting a few minutes, he jogged on east again. He caught up with me at Ohio Avenue, where we rested together.

I should say that about seven hundred people passed us. A funny thing was that all of them were on foot. Nobody seemed to have had the courage to stop and start his car; but as I remember it, all cars had to be cranked in those days, which is probably the reason.'

The next day, the city went about its business as if nothing had happened, but there was no joking. It was two years or more before you dared treat the breaking of the dam lightly. And even now, twenty years after, there are a few persons, like Dr Mallory, who will shut up like a clam if you mention the Afternoon of the Great Run.

The Departure of
Emma Inch

EMMA INCH looked no different from any other middle-aged, thin woman you might glance at in the subway or deal with across the counter of some small store in a country town, and then forget forever. Her hair was drab and unabundant, her face made no impression on you, her voice I don't remember – it was just a voice. She came to us with a letter of recommendation from some acquaintance who knew that we were going to Martha's Vineyard for the summer and wanted a cook. We took her because there was nobody else, and she seemed all right. She had arrived at our hotel in Forty-fifth Street the day before we were going to leave and we got her a room for the night, because she lived way uptown somewhere. She said she really ought to go back and give up her room, but I told her I'd fix that.

Emma Inch had a big scuffed brown suitcase with her, and a Boston bull terrier. His name was Feely. Feely was seventeen years old and he grumbled and growled and snuffled all the time, but we needed a cook and we agreed to take Feely along with Emma Inch, if she would take care of him and keep him out of the way. It turned out to be easy to keep Feely out of the way because he would lie grousing anywhere Emma put him until she came and picked him up

again. I never saw him walk. Emma had owned him, she said, since he was a pup. He was all she had in the world, she told us, with a mist in her eyes. I felt embarrassed but not touched. I didn't see how anybody could love Feely.

I didn't lose any sleep about Emma Inch and Feely the night of the day they arrived, but my wife did. She told me next morning that she had lain awake a long time thinking about the cook and her dog, because she felt kind of funny about them. She didn't know why. She just had a feeling that they were kind of funny. When we were all ready to leave – it was about three o'clock in the afternoon, for we had kept putting off the packing – I phoned Emma's room, but she didn't answer. It was getting late and we felt nervous – the Fall River boat would sail in about two hours. We couldn't understand why we hadn't heard anything from Emma and Feely. It wasn't until four o'clock that we did. There was a small rap on the door of our bedroom and I opened it and Emma and Feely were there, Feely in her arms, snuffing and snaffling, as if he had been swimming a long way.

My wife told Emma to get her bag packed, we were leaving in a little while. Emma said her bag *was* packed, except for her electric fan, and she couldn't get that in. 'You won't need an electric fan at the Vineyard,' my wife told her. 'It's cool there, even during the day, and it's almost cold at night. Besides, there is no electricity in the cottage we are going to.' Emma Inch seemed distressed. She studied my wife's face. 'I'll have to think of something else then,' she said. 'Mebbe I could let the water run all night.' We both sat down and looked at her. Feely's asthmatic noises were the only sounds in the room for a while. 'Doesn't that dog ever stop that?' I asked, irritably. 'Oh, he's just talking,' said Emma. 'He talks all the time, but I'll keep him in my room and he won't bother you none.' 'Doesn't he bother you?' I asked. 'He *would* bother me', said Emma, 'at night, but I put the electric fan on and keep the light burning. He don't make so much noise when it's light, because he don't snore. The fan kind of keeps me from noticing him. I put a piece of cardboard, like, where the fan hits it and then I don't notice Feely so much. Mebbe I could let the water run in my room all night instead of the fan.' I said 'Hmmm' and got up and mixed a drink for my wife and me – we had decided not to have one till we got on the boat, but I thought we'd better have one now. My wife didn't tell Emma there would be no running water in her room at the Vineyard.

'We've been worried about you, Emma,' I said. 'I phoned your room but you didn't answer.' 'I never answer the phone,' said Emma, 'because I always get a shock. I wasn't there anyways. I couldn't sleep in that room. I went back to Mrs McCoy's on Seventy-eighth Street.' I lowered my glass. 'You went back to Seventy-eighth Street last *night*?' I demanded. 'Yes, sir,' she said. 'I had to tell Mrs McCoy I was going away and wouldn't be there any more for a while – Mrs McCoy's the landlady. Anyways I never sleep in a hotel.' She looked around the room. 'They burn down,' she told us.

It came out that Emma Inch had not only gone back to Seventy-eighth Street the night before but had walked all the way, carrying Feely. It had taken her an hour or two, because Feely didn't like to be carried very far at a time, so she had had to stop every block or so and put him down on the sidewalk for a while. It had taken her just as long to walk back to our hotel, too; Feely, it seems, never got up before afternoon — that's why she was so late. She was sorry. My wife and I finished our drinks, looking at each other, and at Feely.

Emma Inch didn't like the idea of riding to Pier 14 in a taxi, but after ten minutes of cajoling and pleading she finally got in. 'Make it go slow,' she said. We had enough time, so I asked the driver to take it easy. Emma kept getting to her feet and I kept pulling her back onto the seat. 'I never been in an automobile before,' she said. 'It goes awful fast.' Now and then she gave a little squeal of fright. The driver turned his head and grinned. 'You're OK wit' me, lady,' he said. Feely growled at him. Emma waited until he had turned away again, and then she leaned over to my wife and whispered. 'They all take cocaine,' she said. Feely began to make a new sound — a kind of high, agonized yelp. 'He's singing,' said Emma. She gave a strange little giggle, but the expression of her face didn't change. 'I wish you had put the Scotch where we could get at it,' said my wife.

If Emma Inch had been afraid of the taxi-cab, she was terrified by the *Priscilla* of the Fall River Line. 'I don't think I can go,' said Emma. 'I don't think I could get on a boat. I didn't know they were so big.' She stood rooted to the pier, clasping Feely. She must have squeezed him too hard, for he screamed — he screamed like a woman. We all jumped. 'It's his ears,' said Emma. 'His ears hurt.' We finally got her on the boat, and once aboard, in the salon, her terror abated somewhat. Then the three parting blasts of the boat whistle rocked lower Manhattan. Emma Inch leaped to her feet and began to run, letting go of her suitcase (which she had refused to give up to a porter) but holding on to Feely. I caught her just as she reached the gangplank. The ship was on its way when I let go of her arm.

It was a long time before I could get Emma to go to her stateroom, but she went at last. It was an inside stateroom, and she didn't seem to mind it. I think she was surprised to find that it was like a room, and had a bed and a chair and washbowl. She put Feely down on the floor. 'I think you'll have to do something about the dog,' I said. 'I think they put them somewhere and you get them when you get off.' 'No, they don't,' said Emma. I guess, in this case, they didn't. I don't know. I shut the door on Emma Inch and Feely, and went away. My wife was drinking straight Scotch when I got to our stateroom.

*

The next morning, cold and early, we got Emma and Feely off the *Priscilla* at Fall River and over to New Bedford in a taxi and onto the little boat for Martha's Vineyard. Each move was as difficult as getting a combative drunken man out of the night club in which he fancies he has been insulted. Emma sat in a chair on the Vineyard boat, as far away from sight of the water as she could get, and closed her eyes and held on to Feely. She had thrown a coat over Feely, not only to keep him warm but to prevent any of the ship's officers from taking him away from her. I went in from the deck at intervals to see how she was. She was all right, or at least all right for her, until five minutes before the boat reached the dock at Woods Hole, the only stop between New Bedford and the Vineyard. Then Feely got sick. Or at any rate Emma said he was sick. He didn't seem to me any different from what he always was – his breathing was just as abnormal and irregular. But Emma said he was sick. There were tears in her eyes. 'He's a very sick dog, Mr Thurman,' she said. 'I'll have to take him home.' I knew by the way she said 'home' what she meant. She meant Seventy-eighth Street.

The boat tied up at Woods Hole and was motionless and we could hear the racket of the deckhands on the dock loading freight. 'I'll get off here,' said Emma, firmly, or with more firmness, anyway, than she had shown yet. I explained to her that we would be home in half an hour, that everything would be fine then, everything would be wonderful. I said Feely would be a new dog. I told her people sent sick dogs to Martha's Vineyard to be cured. But it was no good. 'I'll have to take him off here,' said Emma. 'I always have to take him home when he is sick.' I talked to her eloquently about the loveliness of Martha's Vineyard and the nice houses and the nice people and the wonderful accommodations for dogs. But I knew it was useless. I could tell by looking at her. She was going to get off the boat at Woods Hole.

'You really can't do this,' I said, grimly, shaking her arm. Feely snarled weakly. 'You haven't any money and you don't know where you are. You're a long way from New York. Nobody ever got from Woods Hole to New York alone.' She didn't seem to hear me. She began walking toward the stairs leading to the gangplank, crooning to Feely. 'You'll have to go all the way back on boats,' I said, 'or else take a train, and you haven't any money. If you are going to be so stupid and leave us now, I can't give you any money.' 'I don't want any money, Mr Thurman,' she said. 'I haven't earned any money.' I walked along in irritable silence for a moment; then I gave her some money. I made her take it. We got to the gangplank. Feely snaffled and gurgled. I saw now that his eyes were a little red and moist. I knew it would do no good to summon my wife – not when Feely's health was at stake. 'How do you expect to get home from here?' I almost shouted at Emma Inch as she moved down the gangplank. 'You're way out on the end of Massachusetts.' She stopped and turned around. 'We'll walk,' she said. 'We like to walk, Feely and me.' I just stood still and watched her go.

When I went up on deck, the boat was clearing for the Vineyard. 'How's everything?' asked my wife. I waved a hand in the direction of the dock. Emma Inch was standing there, her suitcase at her feet, her dog under one arm, waving goodbye to us with her free hand. I had never seen her smile before, but she was smiling now.

Casuals of the Keys

IF YOU know the more remote little islands off the Florida coast, you may have met – although I greatly doubt it – Captain Darke. Darrell Darke. His haunted key is, for this reason and that, the most inaccessible of them all. I came upon it quite by chance and doubt that I could find it again. I saw him first that moment when my shining little launch, so impudently summer-resortish, pushed its nose against the lonely pier on which he stood. Tall, dark, melancholy, his white shirt open at the throat, he reminded me instantly of that other solitary wanderer among forgotten islands, the doomed Lord Jim.

I stepped off the boat and he came toward me with a lean brown hand out-thrust. 'I'm Darke,' he said, simply, 'Darrell Darke.' I shook hands with him. He seemed pleased to encounter someone from the outside world. I found out later that no white man had set foot on his remote little key for several years.

He took me to a little thatched hut and waved me to a bamboo chair. It was a pleasant place, with a bed of dried palm leaves, a few withered books, some fishing equipment, and a bright rifle. Darke produced from somewhere a bottle with a greenish heavy liquid in it, and two glasses. 'Opono,' he said, apologetically. 'Made from the sap of the opono tree. Horrible stuff, but kicky.' I asked him if he would care for a touch of Bacardi, of which I had a quart on the launch, and he said he would. I went down and got it. . . .

'A newspaperman, eh?' said Darke, with interest, as I filled up the glasses for the third time. 'You must meet a lot of interesting people.' I really felt that I had met a lot of interesting people and, under slight coaxing, began to tell about them: Gene Tunney, Eddie Rickenbacker, the Grand Duchess Marie, William Gibbs McAdoo. Darke listened to my stories with quick attention, thirsty as he was for news of the colourful civilization which, he told me, he had put behind him twenty years before.

'You must,' I said at last, to be polite, 'have met some interesting people yourself.'

'No,' he said. 'All of a stripe, until you came along. Last chap that put in here, for example, was a little fellow name of Mark Menafee who turned up one day some three years ago in an outboard motor. He was only a trainer of fugitives from justice.' Darke reached for the glass I had filled again.

'I never heard of anyone being that,' I said. 'What did he do?'

'He coached fugitives from justice,' said Darke. 'Seems Menafee could spot one instantly. Take the case of Burt Fredericks he told me about. Fredericks was a bank defaulter from Connecticut. Menafee spotted him on a Havana boat – knew him from his pictures in the papers. "Hello, Burt," says Menatee, casually. Fredericks whirled around. Then he caught himself and stared blankly at Menafee. "My name is

Charles Brandon," he says. Menafee won his confidence and for a fee and his expenses engaged to coach Fredericks not to be caught off his guard and answer to the name of Burt. He'd shadow Fredericks from city to city, contriving to come upon him unexpectedly in dining-rooms, men's lounges, bars, and crowded hotel lobbies. "Why Burt!" Menafee would say, gaily, or "It's old Fredericks!" like someone meeting an old friend after years. Fredericks got so he never let on – unless he was addressed as Charlie or Brandon. Far as I know he was never caught. Menafee made enough to keep going, coaching fugitives, but it was a dullish kind of job.' Darke fell silent. I sat watching him.

'Did you ever meet any other uninteresting people?' I asked.

'There was Harrison Cammery,' said Darke, after a moment. 'He put in here one night in a storm, dressed in full evening clothes. Came from New York – I don't know how. There never was a sign of a boat or anything to show how he got here. He was always that way while he was here, dully incomprehensible. He had the most uninteresting of manias, which is monomania. He was a goldfish-holder.' Darke stopped and seemed inclined to let the story end there.

'What do you mean, a goldfish-holder?' I demanded.

'Cammery had been a professional billiard-player,' said Darke. 'He told me that the strain of developing absolutely nerveless hands finally told on him. He had trained so that he could balance five BB shot on the back of each of his fingers indefinitely. One night, at a party where the host had a bowl of goldfish, the guests got to trying to catch them with one grab of their hand. Nobody could do it until

Cammery tried. He caught up one of the fish and held it lightly in his closed hand. He told me that the wettish fluttering of that fish against the palm of his hand became a thing he couldn't forget. He got to snatching up goldfish and holding them, wherever he went. At length he had to have a bowl of them beside the table when he played his billiard matches, and would hold one between innings the way tennis-players take a mouthful of water. The effect finally was to destroy his muscular precision, so he took to the islands. One day he was gone from here – I don't know how. I was glad enough. A singularly one-track and boring fellow.'

'Who else had put in here?' I asked, filling them up again.

'Early in 1913,' said Darke, after a pause in which he

seemed to make an effort to recall what he was after, 'early in 1913 an old fellow with a white beard – must have been seventy-five or eighty – walked into this hut one day. He was dripping wet. Said he swam over from the mainland and he probably did. It's fifty miles. Lots of boats can be had for the taking along the main coast, but this fellow was apparently too stupid to take one. He was as dull about everything as about that. Used to recite stories word for word – said he wrote them himself. He was a writer like you, but he didn't seem to have met any interesting people. Talked only about himself, where he'd come from, what he'd done. I didn't pay any attention to him. I was glad when, one night, he disappeared. His name was . . .' Darke put his head back and stared at the roof of his hut, striving to remember. 'Oh, yes,' he said. 'His name was Bierce. Ambrose Bierce.'

'You say that was in 1913, early in 1913?' I asked, excitedly.

'Yes, I'm sure of it,' said Darke, 'because it was the same year C-18769 showed up here.'

'Who was C-18769?' I asked.

'It was a carrier pigeon,' said Darke. 'Flew in here one night tuckered by the trip from the mainland, and flopped down on that bed with its beak open, panting hard. It was red-eyed and disheveled. I noticed it had something sizable strapped under its belly and I saw a registration number, on a silver band fastened to its leg: C-18769. When it got rested up it hung around here for quite a while. I didn't pay much attention to it. In those days I used to get the New York papers about once a month off a supply boat that used to put in at an island ten miles from here. I'd row over. One day I saw a notice in one of the papers about this bird. Some concern or other, for a publicity stunt, had arranged to have this bird carry a thousand dollars in hundred-dollar bills from the concern's offices to the place where the bird homed, some five hundred miles away. The bird never got there. The papers had all kinds of theories: the bird had been shot and robbed, it had fallen in the water and drowned, or it had got lost.'

'The last was right,' I said. 'It must have got lost.'

'Lost hell,' said Darke. 'After I read the stories I caught it up one day, suddenly, and examined the packet strapped to it. It only had four hundred and sixty-five dollars left.'

I felt a little weak. Finally, in a small voice, I asked: 'Did you turn it over to the authorities?'

'Certainly not,' said Darrell Darke. 'A man or a bird's life is his own to lead, down here. I simply figured this pigeon for a fool, and let him go. What could he do, after the money was gone? Nothing.' Darke rolled and lighted a cigarette and smoked a while, silently. 'That's the kind of beings you meet with down here,' he said. 'Stupid, dullish, lacking in common sense, fiddling along aimlessly. Menafee, Cammery, Bierce, C-18769 – all the same. It gets monotonous. Tell me more about this Grand Duchess Marie. She must be a most interesting person.'

A Preface to Dogs

AS SOON as a wife presents her husband with a child, her capacity for worry becomes acuter: she hears more burglars, she smells more things burning, she begins to wonder, at the theater or the dance, whether her husband left his service revolver in the nursery. This goes on for years and years. As the child grows older, the mother's original major fear – that the child was exchanged for some other infant at the hospital – gives way to even more magnificent doubts and suspicions: she suspects that the child is not bright, she doubts that it will be happy, she is sure that it will become mixed up with the wrong sort of people.

This insistence of parents on dedicating their lives to their children is carried on year after year in the face of all that dogs have done, and are doing, to prove how much happier the parent-child relationship can become if managed without sentiment, worry, or dedication. Of course, the theory that dogs have a saner family life than humans is an old one, and it was in order to ascertain whether the notion is pure legend or whether it is based on observable fact that I have for many years made a careful study of the family life of dogs. My conclusions entirely support the theory that dogs have a saner family life than people.

In the first place, the husband leaves on a woodchuck-hunting expedition just as soon as he can, which is very soon, and never comes back. He doesn't write, makes no provision for the care or maintenance of his family, and is not liable to prosecution because he doesn't. The wife doesn't care where he is, never wonders if he is thinking about her, and although she may start at the slightest footstep, doesn't do so because she is hoping against hope that it is Spot. No lady dog has ever been known to set her friends against her husband or put detectives on his trail.

This same lack of sentimentality is carried out in the mother dog's relationship to her young. For six weeks – but only six weeks – she looks after them religiously, feeds them (they come clothed), washes their ears, fights off cats, old women, and wasps that come noising around, makes the bed, and rescues the puppies when they crawl under the floorboards of the barn or get lost in an old boot. She does all these things, however, without fuss, without that loud and elaborate show of solicitude and alarm which a woman displays in rendering some exaggerated service to her child.

At the end of six weeks the mother dog ceases to lie awake at night harking for ominous sounds; the next morning she snarls at the puppies after breakfast, and routs them all out of the house. 'This is forever,' she informs them succinctly. 'I have my own life to live, automobiles to chase, grocery boys' shoes to snap at, rabbits to pursue. I can't be washing and feeding a lot of big six-week-old dogs any longer. That phase is definitely over.' The family life is thus terminated, and the mother dismisses the children from her mind – frequently as many as eleven at one time – as easily as she

did her husband. She is now free to devote herself to her career and to the novel and astonishing things of life.

In the case of one family of dogs that I observed, the mother, a large black dog with long ears and a keen zest for living, tempered only by an immoderate fear of toads and turtles, kicked ten puppies out of the house at the end of six weeks to the day – it was a Monday. Fortunately for my observations, the puppies had no place to go, since they hadn't made any plans, and so they just hung around the barn, now and again trying to patch things up with their mother. She refused however, to entertain any proposition leading to a resumption of home life, pointing out firmly that she was by inclination a chaser of bicycles and a hearth-fire-watcher, both of which activities would be insupportably cluttered up by the presence of ten helpers. The bicycle-chasing field was overcrowded, anyway, she explained, and the hearth-fire-watching field even more so. 'We could chase parades together,' suggested one of the dogs, but she refused to be touched, snarled, and drove him off.

It is only for a few weeks that the cast-off puppies make overtures to their mother in regard to the re-establishment of a home. At the end of that time, by some natural miracle that I am unable clearly to understand, the puppies suddenly one day don't recognize their mother any more, and she doesn't recognize them. It is as if they had never met, and is a fine idea, giving both parties a clean break and a chance for a fresh start. Once, some months after this particular family had broken up, and the pups had been sold, one of them, named Liza, was brought back to 'the old nest' for a visit. The mother dog of course didn't recognize the puppy and promptly bit her in the hip. They were separated, each grumbling something about you never know what kind of dogs you're going to meet. Here was no silly affecting reunion, no sentimental tears, no bitter intimations of neglect or forgetfulness or desertion.

If a pup is not sold or given away, but is brought up in the same household with its mother, the two will fight bitterly, sometimes twenty or thirty times a day, for maybe a month. This is very trying to whoever owns the dogs, particularly if they are sentimentalists who grieve because mother and child don't know each other. The condition finally clears up: the two dogs grow to tolerate each other and, beyond growling a little under their breath about how it takes all kinds of dogs to make up a world, get along fairly well together when their paths cross. I know of one mother

'At the end of six weeks she tells them to get out
and stay out'

dog and her half-grown daughter who sometimes spend the
whole day together hunting woodchucks, although they
don't speak. Their association is not sentimental, but practical, and is based on the fact that it is safer to hunt woodchucks in pairs than alone. These two dogs start out together
in the morning, without a word, and come back together in
the evening, when they part without saying good night,
whether they have had any luck or not. Avoidance of fare-
wells, which are always stuffy and sometimes painful, is
another thing in which it seems to me dogs have better
sense than people.

Well, one day, the daughter, a dog about ten months old, seemed, by some prank of nature which again I am unable clearly to understand, for a moment or two to recognize her mother after all those months of oblivion. The two had just started out after a fat woodchuck who lived in the orchard. Something felt wrong with the daughter's ear – a long, floppy ear. 'Mother,' she said, 'I wish you'd look at my ear.'

Instantly the other dog bristled and growled. 'I'm not your mother,' she said. 'I'm a woodchuck-hunter.'

The daughter grinned. 'Well,' she said, just to show that there were no hard feelings, 'that's not my ear, it's a short-stop's glove.'

The Private Life of Mr Bidwell

FROM WHERE she was sitting, Mrs Bidwell could not see her husband, but she had a curious feeling of tension: she knew he was up to something.

'What are you doing, George?' she demanded, her eyes still on her book.

'Mm?'

'What's the matter with you?'

'Pahhhhh-h-h,' said Mr Bidwell, in a long, pleasurable exhale. 'I was holding my breath.'

Mrs Bidwell twisted creakingly in her chair and looked at him, he was sitting behind her in his favorite place under the parchment lamp with the street scene of old New York on it. 'I was just holding my breath,' he said again.

'Well, please don't do it,' said Mrs Bidwell, and went back to her book. There was silence for five minutes.

'George!' said Mrs Bidwell.

'Bwaaaaaa,' said Mr Bidwell. 'What?'

'Will you please *stop* that?' she said. 'It makes me nervous.'

'I don't see how that bothers you,' he said. 'Can't I breathe?'

'You can breathe without holding your breath like a goop,' said Mrs Bidwell. 'Goop' was a word that she was fond of using; she rather lazily applied it to everything. It annoyed Mr Bidwell.

'Deep breathing,' said Mr Bidwell, in the impatient tone he used when explaining anything to his wife, 'is good exercise. You ought to take more exercise.'

'Well, please don't do it around me,' said Mrs Bidwell, turning again to the pages of Mr Galsworthy.

At the Cowans' party, a week later, the room was full of chattering people when Mrs Bidwell, who was talking to Lida Carroll, suddenly turned around as if she had been summoned. In a chair in a far corner of the room, Mr Bidwell was holding his breath. His chest was expanded, his chin drawn in; there was a strange stare in his eyes, and his face was slightly empurpled. Mrs Bidwell moved into the

line of his vision and gave him a sharp, penetrating look. He deflated slowly and looked away.

Later, in the car, after they had driven in silence a mile or more on the way home, Mrs Bidwell said, 'It seems to me you might at least have the kindness not to hold your breath in other people's houses.'

'I wasn't hurting anybody,' said Mr Bidwell.

'You looked silly!' said his wife. 'You looked perfectly crazy!' She was driving and she began to speed up, as she always did when excited or angry. 'What do you suppose people thought – you sitting there all swelled up, with your eyes popping out?'

'I wasn't all swelled up,' he said, angrily.

'You looked like a goop,' she said. The car slowed down, sighed, and came to a complete, despondent stop.

'We're out of gas,' said Mrs Bidwell. It was bitterly cold and nastily sleeting. Mr Bidwell took a long, deep breath.

The breathing situation in the Bidwell family reached a critical point when Mr Bidwell began to inhale in his sleep, slowly, and exhale with a protracted, growling 'wooooooo.' Mrs Bidwell, ordinarily a sound sleeper (except on nights when she was sure burglars were getting in), would wake up and reach over and shake her husband. 'George!' she would say.

'Hawwwwww,' Mr Bidwell would say, thickly. 'Wahs maa nah, hm?'

After he had turned over and gone back to sleep, Mrs Bidwell would lie awake, thinking.

One morning at breakfast she said, 'George, I'm not going

to put up with this another day. If you can't stop blowing up like a grampus, I'm going to leave you.' There was a slight, quick lift in Mr Bidwell's heart, but he tried to look surprised and hurt.

'All right,' he said. 'Let's not talk about it.'

Mrs Bidwell buttered another piece of toast. She described to him the way he sounded in his sleep. He read the paper.

With considerable effort, Mr Bidwell kept from inflating his chest for about a week, but one night at the McNallys' he hit on the idea of seeing how many seconds he could hold his breath. He was rather bored by the McNallys' party, anyway. He began timing himself with his wrist-watch in a remote corner of the living-room. Mrs Bidwell, who was in the kitchen talking children and clothes with Bea McNally, left her abruptly and slipped back into the living-room. She stood quietly behind her husband's chair. He knew she was there, and tried to let out his breath imperceptibly.

'I see you,' she said, in a low, cold tone. Mr Bidwell jumped up.

'Why don't you let me alone?' he demanded.

'Will you please lower your voice?' she said, smiling so that if anyone were looking he wouldn't think the Bidwells were arguing.

'I'm getting pretty damned tired of this,' said Bidwell in a low voice.

'You've ruined my evening!' she whispered.

'You've ruined mine, too!' he whispered back. They knifed

each other, from head to stomach, with their eyes.

'Sitting here like a goop, holding your breath,' said Mrs Bidwell. 'People will think you are an idiot.' She laughed, turning to greet a lady who was approaching them.

Mr Bidwell sat in his office the next afternoon, a black, moist afternoon, tapping a pencil on his desk, and scowling. 'All right, then, get out, get out!' he muttered. 'What do I care?' He was visualizing the scene when Mrs Bidwell would walk out on him. After going through it several times, he returned to his work, feeling vaguely contented. He made up his mind to breathe any way he wanted to, no matter what she did. And, having come to this decision, he oddly enough, and quite without effort, lost interest in holding his breath.

Everything went rather smoothly at the Bidwells' for a month or so. Mr Bidwell didn't do anything to annoy his wife beyond leaving his razor on her dressing-table and forgetting to turn out the hall light when he went to bed. Then there came the night of the Bentons' party.

Mr Bidwell, bored as usual, was sitting in a far corner of the room, breathing normally. His wife was talking animatedly with Beth Williamson about negligees. Suddenly her voice slowed and an uneasy look came into her eyes: George was up to something. She turned around and sought him out. To anyone but Mrs Bidwell he must have seemed like any husband sitting in a chair. But his wife's lips set tightly. She walked casually over to him.

'What are you doing?' she demanded.

'Hm?' he said, looking at her vacantly.

'What are you *doing*?' she demanded, again. He gave her a harsh, venomous look, which she returned.

'I'm multiplying numbers in my head,' he said, slowly and evenly, 'if you must know.' In the prolonged, probing examination that they silently, without moving any muscles save those of their eyes, gave each other, it became solidly, frozenly apparent to both of them that the end of their endurance had arrived. The curious bond that held them together snapped – rather more easily than either had supposed was possible. That night, while undressing for bed, Mr Bidwell calmly multiplied numbers in his head. Mrs Bidwell stared coldly at him for a few moments, holding a stocking in her hand; she didn't bother to berate him. He paid no attention to her. The thing was simply over.

George Bidwell lives alone now (his wife remarried). He never goes to parties any more, and his old circle of friends rarely sees him. The last time that any of them did see him, he was walking along a country road with the halting, uncertain gait of a blind man: he was trying to see how many steps he could take without opening his eyes.

The Curb in the Sky

WHEN CHARLIE Deshler announced that he was going to marry Dorothy, someone said he would lose his mind posthaste. 'No,' said a wit who knew them both, 'post hoc.' Dorothy had begun, when she was quite young, to finish sentences for people. Sometimes she finished them wrongly, which annoyed the person who was speaking, and sometimes she finished them correctly, which annoyed the speaker even more.

'When William Howard Taft was—' some guest in Dorothy's family's home would begin.

'President!' Dorothy would pipe up. The speaker may have meant to say 'President' or he may have meant to say 'young,' or 'Chief Justice of the Supreme Court of the United States.' In any case, he would shortly put on his hat and go home. Like most parents, Dorothy's parents did not seem to be conscious that her mannerism was a nuisance. Very likely they thought that it was cute, or even bright. It is even probable that when Dorothy's mother first said 'Come, Dorothy, eat your—' and Dorothy said 'Spinach, dear,' the former telephoned Dorothy's father at the office and told him about it, and he told everybody he met that day about it – and the next day and the day after.

When Dorothy grew up she became quite pretty and so even more of a menace. Gentlemen became attracted to her and then attached to her. Emotionally she stirred them, but mentally she soon began to wear them down. Even in her late teens she began correcting their English. 'Not "was," Arthur,' she would say, '"were." "Were prepared." See?' Most of her admirers tolerated this habit because of their interest in her lovely person, but as time went on and her interest in them remained more instructive than sentimental, they slowly drifted away to less captious, if dumber, girls.

Charlie Deshler, however, was an impetuous man, of the sweep-them-off-their-feet persuasion, and he became engaged to Dorothy so quickly and married her in so short a time that, being deaf to the warnings of friends, whose concern he regarded as mere jealousy, he really didn't know anything about Dorothy except that she was pretty and bright-eyed and (to him) desirable.

Dorothy as a wife came, of course, into her great flowering: she took to correcting Charlie's stories. He had traveled widely and experienced greatly and was a truly excellent *raconteur*. Dorothy was, during their courtship, genuinely interested in him and in his stories, and since she had never shared any of the adventures he told about, she could not know when he made mistakes in time or in place or in identities. Beyond suggesting a change here and there in the number of a verb, she more or less let him alone. Charlie spoke rather good English, anyway – he knew when to say 'were' and when to say 'was' after 'if' – and this was another reason he didn't find Dorothy out.

*

I didn't call on them for quite a while after they were married, because I liked Charlie and I knew I would feel low if I saw him coming out of the anesthetic of her charms and beginning to feel the first pains of reality. When I did finally call, conditions were, of course, all that I had feared. Charlie began to tell, at dinner, about a motor trip the two had made to this town and that – I never found out for sure what towns, because Dorothy denied almost everything that Charlie said. 'The next day,' he would say, 'we got an early start and drove two hundred miles to Fairview—' 'Well,' Dorothy would say, 'I wouldn't call it *early*. It wasn't as early as the first day we set out, when we got up about *seven*. And we only drove a hundred and eighty miles,

73

because I remember looking at that mileage thing when we started.'

'Anyway, when we got to Fairview—' Charlie would go on. But Dorothy would stop him. 'Was it Fairview that day, darling?' she would ask. Dorothy often interrupted Charlie by asking him if he were right, instead of telling him that he was wrong, but it amounted to the same thing, for if he would reply: 'Yes, I'm sure it was Fairview,' she would say: 'But it *wasn't* darling,' and then go on with the story herself. (She called everybody that she differed from 'darling.')

Once or twice, when I called on them or they called on me, Dorothy would let Charlie get almost to the climax of some interesting account of a happening and then, like a tackler from behind, throw him just as he was about to cross the goal-line. There is nothing in life more shocking to the nerves and to the mind than this. Some husbands will sit back amiably – almost it seems, proudly – when their wives interrupt, and let them go on with the story, but these are beaten husbands. Charlie did not become beaten. But his wife's tackles knocked the wind out of him, and he began to realize that he would have to do something. What he did was rather ingenious. At the end of the second year of their marriage, when you visited the Deshlers, Charlie would begin some outlandish story about a dream he had had, knowing that Dorothy could not correct him on his own dreams. They became the only life he had that was his own.

'I thought I was running an airplane,' he would say, 'made out of telephone wires and pieces of old leather. I was trying to make it fly to the moon, taking off from my bedroom. About halfway up to the moon, however, a man who looked like Santa Claus, only he was dressed in the uniform of a customs officer, waved at me to stop – he was in a plane made of telephone wires, too. So I pulled over to a cloud. "Here," he said to me, "you can't go to the moon, if you are the man who invented these wedding cookies." Then he showed me a cookie made in the shape of a man and woman being married – little images of a man and a woman and a minister, made of dough and fastened firmly to a round, crisp cookie base.' So he would go on.

Any psychiatrist will tell you that at the end of the way Charlie was going lies madness in the form of monomania. You can't live in a fantastic dream world, night in and night out and then day in and day out, and remain sane. The substance began to die slowly out of Charlie's life, and he began to live entirely in shadow. And since monomania of this sort is likely to lead in the end to the reiteration of one particular story, Charlie's invention began to grow thin and he eventually took to telling, over and over again, the first dream he had ever described – the story of his curious flight toward the moon in an airplane made of telephone wires. It was extremely painful. It saddened us all.

After a month or two, Charlie finally had to be sent to an asylum. I was out of town when they took him away, but Joe Fultz, who went with him, wrote me about it. 'He seemed to like it up here right away,' Joe wrote. 'He's calmer and his eyes look better.' (Charlie had developed a wild, hunted look.) 'Of course,' concluded Joe, 'he finally got away from that woman.'

It was a couple of weeks later that I drove up to the

asylum to see Charlie. He was lying on a cot on a big screened-in porch, looking wan and thin. Dorothy was sitting on a chair beside his bed, bright-eyed and eager. I was somehow surprised to see her there, having figured that Charlie had, at least, won sanctuary from his wife. He looked quite mad. He began to once to tell me the story of his trip to the moon. He got to the part where the man who looked like Santa Claus waved at him to stop. 'He was in a plane of telephone wires, too,' said Charlie. 'So I pulled over to a curb—'

'No. You pulled over to a *cloud*,' said Dorothy. 'There aren't any curbs in the *sky*. There *couldn't* be. You pulled over to a cloud.'

Charlie sighed and turned slightly in his bed and looked at me. Dorothy looked at me, too, with her pretty smile.

'He always gets that story wrong,' she said.

Mr Preble Gets Rid
of His Wife

MR PREBLE was a plump middle-aged lawyer in Scarsdale. He used to kid with his stenographer about running away with him. 'Let's run away together,' he would say, during a pause in dictation. 'All righty,' she would say.

One rainy Monday afternoon, Mr Preble was more serious about it than usual.

'Let's run away together, said Mr Preble.

'All righty,' said his stenographer. Mr Preble jingled the keys in his pocket and looked out the window.

'My wife would be glad to get rid of me,' he said.

'Would she give you a divorce?' asked the stenographer.

'I don't suppose so,' he said. The stenographer laughed.

'You'd have to get rid of your wife,' she said.

Mr Preble was unusually silent at dinner that night. About half an hour after coffee, he spoke without looking up from his paper.

'Let's go down in the cellar,' Mr Preble said to his wife.

'What for?' she said, not looking up from her book.

'Oh, I don't know,' he said. 'We never go down in the cellar any more. The way we used to.'

'We never did go down in the cellar that I remember,' said

Mrs Preble. 'I could rest easy the balance of my life if I never went down in the cellar.' Mr Preble was silent for several minutes.

'Supposing I said it meant a whole lot to me,' began Mr Preble.

'What's come over you?' his wife demanded. 'It's cold down there and there is absolutely nothing to do.'

'We could pick up pieces of coal,' said Mr Preble. 'We might get up some kind of a game with pieces of coal.'

'I don't want to,' said his wife. 'Anyway, I'm reading.'

'Listen,' said Mr Preble, rising and walking up and down. 'Why won't you come down in the cellar? You can read down there, as far as that goes.'

'There isn't a good enough light down there,' she said, 'and anyway, I'm not going to go down in the cellar. You may as well make up your mind to that.'

'Gee whiz!' said Mr Preble, kicking at the edge of a rug. 'Other people's wives go down in the cellar. Why is it you never want to do anything? I come home worn out from the office and you won't even go down in the cellar with me. God knows it isn't very far – it isn't as if I was asking you to go to the movies or some place.'

'I don't want to *go*!' shouted Mrs Preble. Mr Preble sat down on the edge of a davenport.

'All right, all *right*,' he said. He picked up the newspaper again. 'I wish you'd let me tell you more about it. It's – kind of a surprise.'

'Will you quit harping on that subject?' asked Mrs Preble.

'Listen,' said Mr Preble, leaping to his feet. 'I might as well tell you the truth instead of beating around the bush. I want to get rid of you so I can marry my stenographer. Is there anything especially wrong about that? People do it every day. Love is something you can't control—'

'We've been all over that,' said Mrs Preble. 'I'm not going to go all over that again.'

'I just wanted you to know how things are,' said Mr Preble. 'But you have to take everything so literally. Good Lord, do you suppose I really wanted to go down in the cellar and make up some silly game with pieces of coal?'

'I never believed that for a minute,' said Mrs Preble. 'I knew all along you wanted to get me down there and bury me.'

'You can say that now – after I told you,' said Mr Preble. 'But it would never have occurred to you if I hadn't.'

'You didn't tell me; I got it out of you,' said Mrs Preble. 'Anyway, I'm always two steps ahead of what you're thinking.'

'You're never within a mile of what I'm thinking,' said Mr Preble.

'Is that so? I knew you wanted to bury me the minute you set foot in this house tonight.' Mrs Preble held him with a glare.

'Now that's just plain damn exaggeration,' said Mr Preble, considerably annoyed. 'You knew nothing of the sort. As a matter of fact, I never thought of it till just a few minutes ago.'

'It was in the back of your mind,' said Mrs Preble. 'I suppose this filing woman put you up to it.'

'You needn't get sarcastic,' said Mr Preble. 'I have plenty of people to file without having her file. She doesn't know anything about this. She isn't in on it. I was going to tell her you had gone to visit some friends and fell over a cliff. She wants me to get a divorce.'

'That's a laugh,' said Mrs Preble. '*That's* a laugh. You may bury me, but you'll never get a divorce.'

'She knows that! I told her that,' said Mr Preble. 'I mean – I told her I'd never get a divorce.'

'Oh, you probably told her about burying me, too,' said Mrs Preble.

'That's not true,' said Mr Preble, with dignity. 'That's between you and me. I was never going to tell a soul.'

'You'd blab it to the whole world; don't tell me,' said Mrs Preble. 'I know you.' Mr Preble puffed at his cigar.

'I wish you were buried now and it was all over with,' he said.

'Don't you suppose you would get caught, you crazy thing?' she said. 'They always get caught. Why don't you go to bed? You're just getting yourself worked up over nothing.'

'I'm not going to bed,' said Mr Preble. 'I'm going to bury you in the cellar. I've got my mind made up to it. I don't know how I could make it any plainer.'

'Listen,' cried Mrs Preble, throwing her book down, 'will you be satisfied and shut up if I go down in the cellar? Can I have a little peace if I go down in the cellar? Will you let me alone then?'

'Yes,' said Mr Preble. 'But you spoil it by taking that attitude.'

'Sure, sure, I always spoil everything. I stop reading right in the middle of a chapter. I'll never know how the story comes out – but that's nothing to you.'

'Did I make you start reading the book?' asked Mr Preble.

He opened the cellar door. 'Here, you go first.'

'Brrr,' said Mrs Preble, starting down the steps. 'It's *cold* down here! You *would* think of this, at this time of year! Any other husband would have buried their wife in the summer.'

'You can't arrange those things just whenever you want to,' said Mr Preble. 'I didn't fall in love with this girl till late fall.'

'Anybody else would have fallen in love with her long before that. She's been around for years. Why is it you always let other men get in ahead of you? Mercy, but it's dirty down here! What have you got there?'

'I was going to hit you over the head with this shovel,' said Mr Preble.

'You were, huh?' said Mrs Preble. 'Well, get that out of your mind. Do you want to leave a great big clue right here in the middle of everything where the first detective that comes snooping around will find it? Go out in the street and find some piece of iron or something – something that doesn't belong to you.'

'Oh, all right,' said Mr Preble. 'But there won't be any piece of iron in the street. Women always expect to pick up a piece of iron anywhere.'

'If you look in the right place you'll find it,' said Mrs Preble. 'And don't be gone long. Don't you dare stop in at the cigarstore. I'm not going to stand down here in this cold cellar all night and freeze.'

'All right,' said Mr Preble. 'I'll hurry.'

'And shut that *door* behind you!' she screamed after him. 'Where were you born – in a barn?'

A Portrait of Aunt Ida

MY MOTHER'S Aunt Ida Clemmens died the other day out West. She was ninety-one years old. I remember her clearly, although I haven't thought about her in a long time and never saw her after I was twenty. I remember how dearly she loved catastrophes, especially those of a national or international importance. The sinking of the *Titanic* was perhaps the most important tragedy of the years in which I knew her. She never saw in such things, as her older sisters, Emma and Clara, did, the vengeance of a Deity outraged by Man's lust for speed and gaiety; she looked for the causes deep down in the dark heart of the corporate interests. You could never make her believe that the *Titanic* hit an iceberg. Whoever *heard* of such a thing! It was simply a flimsy prevarication devised to cover up the real cause. The real cause she could not, or would not, make plain, but somewhere in its black core was a monstrous secret of treachery and corrupt goings-on – men were like that. She came later on to doubt the courage of the brave gentlemen on the sinking ship who at the last waved goodbye smilingly and smoked cigarettes. It was her growing conviction that most of them had to be shot by the ship's officers in order to prevent them from crowding into the lifeboats ahead of the older and less attractive women passengers. Eminence and wealth in men Aunt Ida persistently attributed to deceit, trickery, and impiety. I think the only famous person she ever trusted in her time was President McKinley.

The disappearance of Judge Crater, the Hall-Mills murder, the Starr Faithfull case, and similar mysteries must have made Aunt Ida's last years happy. She loved the unsolvable and the unsolved. Mysteries that were never cleared up were brought about, in her opinion, by the workings of some strange force in the world which we do not thoroughly understand and which God does not intend that we ever shall understand. An invisible power, a power akin to electricity and radio (both of which she must have regarded as somehow or other blasphemous), but never to be isolated or channeled. Out of this power came murder, disappearances, and supernatural phenomena. All persons connected in any way whatever with celebrated cases were tainted in Aunt Ida's sight – and that went for prosecuting attorneys, too (always 'tricky' men). But she would, I'm sure, rather have had a look at Willie Stevens than at President Roosevelt, at Jafsie than at the King of England, just as she would rather have gone through the old Wendel house than the White House.

Surgical operations and post-mortems were among Aunt Ida's special interests, although she did not believe that any operation was ever necessary and she was convinced that post-mortems were conducted to cover up something rather than to find something out. It was her conviction that doctors were in the habit of trying to obfuscate or

distort the true facts about illness and death. She believed
that many of her friends and relatives had been laid away
without the real causes of their deaths being entered on the
'city books.' She was fond of telling a long and involved
story about the death of one of her first cousins, a married
woman who had passed away at twenty-five. Aunt Ida for
thirty years contended that there was something 'behind
it.' She believed that a certain physician, a gentleman of the
highest reputation, would some day 'tell the truth about
Ruth,' perhaps on his deathbed. When he died (without
confessing, of course), she said after reading the account in
the newspaper that she had dreamed of him a few nights
before. It seemed that he had called to her and wanted to
tell her something but couldn't.

Aunt Ida believed that she was terribly psychic. She had
warnings, premonitions, and 'feelings.' They were invariably
intimations of approaching misfortune, sickness, or death.
She never had a premonition that everything was going to
be all right. It was always that Grace So-and-So was not
going to marry the man she was engaged to, or that Mr
Hollowell, who was down in South America on business,
would never return, or that old Mrs Hutchins would not
last out the year (she missed on old Mrs Hutchins for
twenty-two years but finally made it). Most all of Aunt
Ida's forewarnings of financial ruin and marital tragedy
came in the daytime while she was marketing or sitting
hulling peas; most all of her intimations of death appeared
to her in dreams. Dreams of Ohio women of Aunt Ida's
generation were never Freudian; they were purely prophetic.
They dealt with black hearses and white hearses rolling

soundlessly along through the night, and with coffins being carried out of houses, and with tombstones bearing names and dates, and with tall, faceless women in black veils and gloves. Most of Aunt Ida's dreams foretold the fate of women, for what happened to women was of much greater importance to Aunt Ida than what happened to men. Men usually 'brought things on themselves'; women, on the other hand, were usually the victims of dark and devious goings-on of a more or less supernatural nature.

Birth was, in some ways, as dark a matter to Aunt Ida as death. She felt that most babies, no matter what you said or anybody else said, were 'not wanted.' She believed that the children of famous people, brilliant people, and of first, second, or third cousins would be idiotic. If a child died young, she laid it to the child's parentage, no matter what the immediate cause of death might have been. 'There is something in that family,' Aunt Ida used to say, in her best funeral voice. This something was a vague, ominous thing, both far off and close at hand, misty and ready to spring, compounded of nobody could guess exactly what. One of Aunt Ida's favorite predictions was 'They'll never raise that baby, you mark my words.' The fact that they usually did never shook her confidence in her 'feeling.' If she was right once in twenty times, it proved that she knew what she was talking about. In foretelling the sex of unborn children, she was right about half the time.

Life after death was a source of speculation, worry and exhilaration to Aunt Ida. She firmly believed that people could 'come back' and she could tell you of many a house that was haunted (barrels of apples rolled down the attic steps of one of them, I remember, but it was never clear why they did). Aunt Ida put no faith in mediums or séances. The dead preferred to come back to the houses where they had lived and to go stalking through the rooms and down the halls. I think Aunt Ida always thought of them as coming back in the flesh, fully clothed, for she always spoke of them as 'the dead,' never as ghosts. The reason they came back was that they had left something unsaid or undone that must be corrected. Although a descendent of staunch orthodox Methodists, some of them ministers, Aunt Ida in her later years dabbled a little in various religions, superstitions, and even cults. She found astrology, New Thought, and the theory of reincarnation comforting. The people who are bowed down in this life, she grew to believe, will have another chance.

Aunt Ida was confident that the world was going to be destroyed almost any day. When Halley's comet appeared in 1910, she expected to read in the papers every time she picked them up the news that Paris had gone up in flames and that New York City had slid into the ocean. Those two cities, being horrible dens of vice, were bound to go first; the smaller towns would be destroyed in a more leisurely fashion with some respectable and dignified ending for the pious and the kindly people.

Two of Aunt Ida's favorite expressions were 'I never heard of such a thing' and 'If I never get up from this chair . . .' She told all stories of death, misfortune, grief, corruption, and disaster with vehemence and exaggeration. She was hampered in narration by her inability to think of names, particularly simple names, such as Joe, Earl, Ned, Harry, Louise, Ruth, Bert. Somebody usually had to prompt her with the name of the third cousin, or whomever, that she was trying to think of, but she was unerring in her ability to remember difficult names the rest of us had long forgotten. 'He used to work in the old Schirtzberger & Wallenheim saddle store in Naughton Street,' she would say. 'What *was* his name?' It would turn out that his name was Frank Butler.

Up to the end, they tell me, Aunt Ida could read without her glasses, and none of the commoner frailties of senility affected her. She had no persecution complex, no lapses of memory, no trailing off into the past, no unfounded bitternesses – unless you could call her violent hatred of cigarettes unfounded bitterness, and I don't think it was, because she actually knew stories of young men and even young women who had become paralyzed to the point of losing the use of both legs through smoking cigarettes. She tended to her begonias and wrote out a check for the rent the day she took to her bed for the last time. It irked her not to be up and about, and she accused the doctor the family brought in of not knowing his business. There was marketing to do, and friends to call on, and work to get through with. When friends and relatives began calling on her, she was annoyed. Making out that she was really sick! Old Mrs Kurtz, who is seventy-two, visited her on the last day, and when she left, Aunt Ida looked after her pityingly. 'Poor Cora,' she said, 'she's failin', ain't she?'

The Remarkable Case
of Mr Bruhl

SAMUEL O'BRUHL was just an ordinary-looking citizen, like you and me, except for a curious, shoe-shaped scar on his left cheek, which he got when he fell against a wagon-tongue in his youth. He had a good job as treasurer for a syrup-and-fondant concern, a large, devout wife, two tractable daughters, and a nice home in Brooklyn. He worked from nine to five, took in a show occasionally, played a bad, complacent game of golf, and was usually in bed by eleven o'clock. The Bruhls had a dog named Bert, a small circle of friends, and an old sedan. They had made a comfortable, if unexciting, adjustment to life.

There was no reason in the world why Samuel Bruhl shouldn't have lived along quietly until he died of some commonplace malady. He was a man designed by Nature for an uneventful life, an inexpensive but respectable funeral, and a modest stone marker. All this you would have predicted had you observed his colorless comings and goings, his mild manner, the small stature of his dreams. He was, in brief, the sort of average citizen that observers of Judd Gray thought Judd Gray was. And precisely as that mild little family man was abruptly hurled into an incongruous tragedy, so was Samuel Bruhl suddenly picked out of the hundreds of men just like him and marked for an extravagant and unpredictable end. Oddly enough it was the shoe-shaped scar on his left cheek which brought to his heels a Nemesis he had never dreamed of. A blemish on his heart, a tic in his soul would have been different; one would have blamed Bruhl for whatever anguish an emotional or spiritual flaw laid him open to, but it is ironical indeed when the Furies ride down a man who has been guilty of nothing worse than an accident in his childhood.

Samuel O. Bruhl looked very much like George ('Shoescar') Clinigan. Clinigan had that same singular shoe-shaped scar on his left cheek. There was also a general resemblance in height, weight, and complexion. A careful study would have revealed very soon that Clinigan's eyes were shifty and Bruhl's eyes were clear, and that the syrup-and-fondant

company's treasurer had a more pleasant mouth and a higher forehead than the gangster and racketeer, but at a glance the similarity was remarkable.

Had Clinigan not become notorious, this prank of Nature would never have been detected, but Clinigan did become notorious and dozens of persons observed that he looked like Bruhl. They saw Clinigan's picture in the papers the day he was shot, and the day after, and the day after that. Presently someone in the syrup-and-fondant concern mentioned to someone else that Clinigan looked like Mr Bruhl, remarkably like Mr Bruhl. Soon everybody in the place had commenced on it, among themselves, and to Mr Bruhl.

Mr Bruhl rather laughed it off at first, but one day when Clinigan had been in the hospital a week, a cop peered closely at Mr Bruhl when he was on his way home from work. After that, the little treasurer noticed a number of other strangers staring at him with mingled surprise and alarm. One small, dark man hastily thrust a hand into his coat pocket and paled slightly.

Mr Bruhl began to worry. He began to imagine things. 'I hope this fellow Clinigan doesn't pull through,' he said one morning at breakfast. 'He's a bad actor. He's better off dead.'

'Oh, he'll pull through,' said Mrs Bruhl, who had been reading the morning paper. 'It says here he'll pull through. But it says they'll shoot him again. It says they're sure to shoot him again.'

The morning after the night that Clinigan left the hospital, secretly, by a side door, and disappeared into the town, Bruhl decided not to go to work. 'I don't feel so good today,' he said to his wife. 'Would you call up the office and tell them I'm sick?'

'You don't look well,' said his wife. 'You really don't look well. Get down, Bert,' she added, for the dog had jumped upon her lap and whined. The animal knew that something was wrong.

That evening Bruhl, who had mooned about the house all day, read in the papers that Clinigan had vanished, but was believed to be somewhere in the city. His various rackets required his presence, at least until he made enough money to skip out with; he had left the hospital penniless. Rival gangsters, the papers said, were sure to seek him out, to hunt him down, to give it to him again. 'Give him what again?' asked Mrs Bruhl when she read this. 'Let's talk about something else,' said her husband.

It was little Joey, the officeboy at the syrup-and-fondant company, who first discovered that Mr Bruhl was afraid. Joey, who went about with tennis shoes on, entered the treasurer's office suddenly – flung open the door and started to say something. 'Good God!' cried Mr Bruhl, rising from his chair. 'Why, what's the matter, Mr Bruhl?' asked Joey. Other little things happened. The switchboard girl phoned Mr Bruhl's desk one afternoon and said there was a man waiting to see him, a Mr Globe. 'What's he look like?' asked Bruhl, who didn't know anybody named Globe. 'He's small and dark,' said the girl. 'A small, dark man?' said Bruhl. 'Tell him I'm out. Tell him I've gone to California.' The personnel, comparing notes, decided at length that the treasurer was afraid of being mistaken for Shoescar and put on the spot. They said nothing to Mr Bruhl about this, because they were forbidden to by Ollie Breithofter, a fattish clerk who was a tireless and inventive practical joker and who had an idea.

As the hunt went on for Clinigan and he still wasn't found and killed, Mr Bruhl lost weight and grew extremely fidgety. He began to figure out new ways of getting to work, one requiring the use of two different ferry lines; he ate his lunch in, he wouldn't answer bells, he cried out when anyone dropped anything, and he ran into stores or banks when cruising taxi-drivers shouted at him. One morning, in setting the house to rights, Mrs Bruhl found a revolver under his pillow. 'I found a revolver under your pillow,' she told him that night. 'Burglars are bad in this neighborhood,' he said. 'You oughtn't to have a revolver,' she said. They argued about it, he irritably, she uneasily, until time for bed. As Bruhl was undressing, after locking and bolting all the doors, the telephone rang. 'It's for you, Sam,' said Mrs Bruhl. Her husband went slowly to the phone, passing Bert on the way. 'I wish I was you,' he said to the dog, and took up the receiver. 'Get this, Shoescar,' said a husky voice. 'We trailed you where you are, see? You're cooked.' The receiver at the other end was hung up. Bruhl shouted. His wife came running. 'What is it, Sam, what is it?' she cried. Bruhl, pale, sick-looking, had fallen into a chair. 'They got me,' he moaned. 'They got me.' Slowly, deviously, Minnie Bruhl got it out of her husband that he had been mistaken for Clinigan and that he was cooked. Mrs Bruhl was not very quick mentally, but she had a certain intuition and this intuition told her, as she trembled there in her nightgown above her broken husband, that this was the work of Ollie

Breithofter. She instantly phoned Ollie Breithofer's wife and, before she hung up, had got the truth out of Mrs Breithofer. It was Ollie who had called.

The treasurer of the Maskonsett Syrup & Fondant Company, Inc., was so relieved to know that the gangs weren't after him that he admitted frankly at the office next day that Ollie had fooled him for a minute. Mr Bruhl even joined in the laughter and wisecracking, which went on all day. After that, for almost a week, the mild little man had comparative peace of mind. The papers said very little about Clinigan now. He had completely disappeared. Gang warfare had died down for the time being.

One Sunday morning Mr Bruhl went for an automobile ride with his wife and daughters. They had driven about a mile through Brooklyn streets when, glancing in the mirror above his head, Mr Bruhl observed a blue sedan just behind him. He turned off into the next street, and the sedan turned off too. Bruhl made another turn, and the sedan followed him. 'Where are you going, dear?' asked Mrs Bruhl. Mr Bruhl didn't answer her, he speeded up, he drove terrifically fast, he turned corners so wildly that the rear wheels swung around. A traffic cop shrilled at him. The younger daughter screamed. Bruhl drove right on, weaving in and out. Mrs Bruhl began to berate him wildly. 'Have you lost your mind, Sam?' she shouted. Mr Bruhl looked behind him. The sedan was no longer to be seen. He slowed up. 'Let's go home,' he said. 'I've had enough of this.'

A month went by without incident (thanks largely to Mrs Breithofer) and Samuel Bruhl began to be himself again. On the day that he was practically normal once more, Sluggy Pensiotta, alias Killer Lewis, alias Strangler Koetschke, was shot. Sluggy was the leader of the gang that had sworn to get Shoescar Clinigan. The papers instantly took up the gang-war story where they had left off. Pictures of Clinigan were published again. The slaying of Pensiotta, said the papers, meant but one thing: it meant that Shoescar Clinigan was cooked. Mr Bruhl, reading this, went gradually to pieces once more.

After another week of skulking about, starting at every noise, and once almost fainting when an automobile back-fired near him, Samuel Bruhl began to take on a remarkable new appearance. He talked out of the corner of his mouth, his eyes grew shifty. He looked more and more like Shoescar Clinigan. He snarled at his wife. Once he called her 'Babe,' and he had never called her anything but Minnie. He kissed her in a strange, new way, acting rough, almost brutal. At the office he was mean and overbearing. He used peculiar language. One night when the Bruhls had friends in for bridge – old Mr Creegan and is wife – Bruhl suddenly appeared from upstairs with a pair of scarlet pajamas on, smoking a cigarette, and gripping his revolver. After a few loud and incoherent remarks of a boastful nature, he let fly at a clock on the mantel, and hit it squarely in the middle. Mrs Bruhl screamed. Mr Creegan fainted. Bert, who was in the kitchen, howled. 'What's the matta you?' snarled Bruhl. 'Ya bunch of softies.'

Quite by accident, Mrs Bruhl discovered, hidden away in a closet, eight or ten books on gangs and gangsters, which

Bruhl had put there. They included 'Al Capone,' 'You Can't Win,' '10,000 Public Enemies' and a lot of others; and they were all well thumbed. Mrs Bruhl realized that it was high time something was done, and she determined to have a doctor for her husband. For two or three days Bruhl had not gone to work. He lay around in his bedroom, in his red pajamas, smoking cigarettes. The office phoned once or twice. When Mrs Bruhl urged him to get up and dress and go to work, he laughed and patted her roughly on the head. 'It's a knockover, kid,' he said. 'We'll be sitting pretty. To hell with it.'

The doctor who finally came and slipped into Bruhl's bedroom was very grave when he emerged. 'This is a psychosis,' he said, 'a definite psychosis. Your husband is living in a world of fantasy. He has built up a curious defence mechanism against something or other.' The doctor suggested that a psychiatrist be called in, but after he had gone Mrs Bruhl decided to take her husband out of town on a trip. The Maskonsett Syrup & Fondant Company, Inc., was very fine about it. Mr Scully said of course. 'Sam is very valuable to us, Mrs Bruhl,' said Mr Scully, 'and we all hope he'll be all right.' Just the same he had Mr Bruhl's accounts examined, when Mrs Bruhl had gone.

Oddly enough, Samuel Bruhl was amenable to the idea of going away. 'I need a rest,' he said. 'You're right. Let's get the hell out of here.' He seemed normal up to the time they set out for the Grand Central and then he insisted on leaving from the 125th Street station. Mrs Bruhl took exception to this, as being ridiculous, whereupon her doting husband snarled at her. 'God, what a dumb moll *I* picked,' he said to

Minnie Bruhl, and he added bitterly that if the heat was put to him it would be his own babe who was to blame. 'And what do you think of *that*?' he said, pushing her to the floor of the cab.

They went to a little inn in the mountains. It wasn't a very nice place, but the rooms were clean and the meals were good. There was no form of entertainment, except a Tom Thumb golf course and an uneven tennis court, but Mr Bruhl didn't mind. He said it was too cold outdoors, anyway. He stayed indoors, reading and smoking. In the evening he played the mechanical piano in the dining-room. He liked to play 'More Than You Know' over and over again. One night about nine o'clock, he was putting in his seventh or eighth nickel when four men walked into the dining-room. They were silent men, wearing overcoats, and carrying what appeared to be cases for musical instruments. They took out various kinds of guns from their cases, quickly, expertly, and walked over toward Bruhl, keeping step. He turned just in time to see them line up four abreast and aim at him. Nobody else was in the room. There was a cumulative roar and a series of flashes. Mr Bruhl fell and the men walked out in single file, rapidly, nobody having said a word.

Mrs Bruhl, state police, and the hotel manager tried to get the wounded man to talk. Chief Witznitz of the nearest town's police force tried it. It was no good. Bruhl only snarled and told them to go away and let him alone. Finally, Commissioner O'Donnell of the New York City Police Department arrived at the hospital. He asked Bruhl what the men looked like. 'I don't know what they looked like,' snarled

Bruhl, 'and if I did know I wouldn't tell you.' He was silent a moment, then: 'Cop!' he added, bitterly. The Commissioner sighed and turned away. 'They're all like that,' he said to the others in the room. 'They never talk.' Hearing this, Mr Bruhl smiled, a pleased smile, and closed his eyes.

The Greatest Man
in the World

LOOKING BACK on it now, from the vantage point of 1940, one can only marvel that it hadn't happened long before it did. The United States of America had been, ever since Kitty Hawk, blindly constructing the elaborate petard by which, sooner or later, it must be hoist. It was inevitable that some day there would come roaring out of the skies a national hero of insufficient intelligence, background, and character successfully to endure the mounting orgies of glory prepared for aviators who stayed up a long time or flew a great distance. Both Lindbergh and Byrd, fortunately for national decorum and international amity, had been gentlemen; so had our other famous aviators. They wore their laurels gracefully, withstood the awful weather of publicity, married excellent women, usually of fine family, and quietly retired to private life and the environment of their varying fortunes. No untoward incidents, on a worldwide scale, marred the perfection of their conduct on the perilous heights of fame. The exception to the rule was, however, bound to occur and it did, in July, 1937, when Jack ('Pal') Smurch, erstwhile mechanic's helper in a small garage in Westfield, Iowa, flew a second-hand, single-motored Bresthaven Dragon-Fly III monoplane all the way around the world, without stopping.

*

Never before in the history of aviation had such a flight as Smurch's ever been dreamed of. No one had even taken seriously the weird floating auxiliary gas tanks, invention of the mad New Hampshire professor of astronomy, Dr Charles Lewis Gresham, upon which Smurch placed full reliance. When the garage worker, a slightly built, surly, unprepossessing young man of twenty-two, appeared at Roosevelt Field early in July, 1937, slowly chewing a great quid of scrap tobacco, and announced 'Nobody ain't seen no flyin' yet,' the newspapers touched briefly and satirically upon his projected twenty-five-thousand-mile flight. Aeronautical and automotive experts dismissed the idea curtly, implying that it was a hoax, a publicity stunt. The rusty, battered, second-hand plane wouldn't go. The Gresham auxiliary tanks wouldn't work. It was simply a cheap joke.

Smurch, however, after calling on a girl in Brooklyn who worked in the flap-folding department of a large paper-box factory, a girl whom he later described as his 'sweet patootie,' climbed nonchalantly into his ridiculous plane at dawn of the memorable seventh of July, 1937, spit a curve of tobacco juice into the still air, and took off, carrying with him only a gallon of bootleg gin and six pounds of salami.

When the garage boy thundered out over the ocean the papers were forced to record, in all seriousness, that a mad, unknown young man – his name was variously misspelled – had actually set out upon a preposterous attempt to span the world in a rickety, one-engined contraption, trusting to the long-distance refuelling device of a crazy schoolmaster.

When, nine days later, without having stopped once, the tiny plane appeared above San Francisco Bay, headed for New York, spluttering and choking, to be sure, but still magnificently and miraculously aloft, the headlines, which long since had crowded everything else off the front page – even the shooting of the Governor of Illinois by the Vileti gang – swelled to unprecedented size, and the news stories began to run to twenty-five and thirty columns. It was noticeable, however, that the accounts of the epoch-making flight touched rather lightly upon the aviator himself. This was not because facts about the hero as a man were too meager, but because they were too complete.

Reporters, who had been rushed out to Iowa when Smurch's plane was first sighted over the little French coast town of Serly-le-Mer, to dig up the story of the great man's life, had promptly discovered that the story of his life could not be printed. His mother, a sullen short-order cook in a shack restaurant on the edge of a tourists' camping ground near Westfield, met all inquiries as to her son with an angry 'Ah, the hell with him; I hope he drowns.' His father appeared to be in jail somewhere for stealing spotlights and laprobes from tourists' automobiles; his young brother, a weak-minded lad, had but recently escaped from Preston, Iowa, Reformatory and was already wanted in several Western towns for the theft of money-order blanks from post offices. These alarming discoveries were still piling up at the very time that Pal Smurch, the greatest hero of the twentieth century, blear-eyed, dead for sleep, half-starved, was piloting his crazy junk-heap high above the region in which the lamentable story of his private life was being unearthed, headed for New York and a greater glory than any man of his time had ever known.

The necessity for printing some account in the papers of the young man's career and personality had led to a remarkable predicament. It was of course impossible to reveal the facts, for a tremendous popular feeling in favor of the young hero had sprung up, like a grass fire, when he was halfway across Europe on his flight around the globe. He was, therefore, described as a modest chap, taciturn, blond, popular with his friends, popular with girls. The only available snapshot of Smurch, taken at the wheel of a phony automobile in a cheap photo studio at an amusement park, was touched up so that the little vulgarian looked quite handsome. His twisted leer was smoothed into a pleasant smile. The truth was, in this way, kept from the youth's ecstatic compatriots; they did not dream that the Smurch family was despised and feared by its neighbors in the obscure Iowa town, nor that the hero himself, because of numerous unsavory exploits, had come to be regarded in Westfield as a nuisance and a menace. He had, the reporters discovered, once knifed the principal of his high school – not mortally, to be sure, but he had knifed him; and on another occasion, surprised in the act of stealing an altar-cloth from a church, he had bashed the sacristan over the head with a pot of Easter lilies; for each of these offences he had served a sentence in the reformatory.

Inwardly, the authorities, both in New York and in Washington, prayed that an understanding Providence might, however awful such a thing seemed, bring disaster to the rusty, battered plane and its illustrious pilot, whose unheard-of flight had aroused the civilized world to hosannas of hysterical praise. The authorities were convinced that the character of the renowned aviator was such that the limelight of adulation was bound to reveal him, to all the world, as a congenital hooligan mentally and morally unequipped to cope with his own prodigious fame. 'I trust,' said the Secretary of State, at one of many secret Cabinet meetings called to consider the national dilemma, 'I trust that his mother's prayer will be answered,' by which he referred to Mrs Emma Smurch's wish that her son might be drowned. It was, however, too late for that – Smurch had leaped the Atlantic and then the Pacific as if they were millponds. At three minutes after two o'clock on the afternoon of July 17, 1937, the garage boy brought his idiotic plane into Roosevelt Field for a perfect three-point landing.

It had, of course, been out of the question to arrange a modest little reception for the greatest flier in the history of the world. He was received at Roosevelt Field with such elaborate and pretentious ceremonies as rocked the world. Fortunately, however, the worn and spent hero promptly swooned, had to be removed bodily from his plane, and was spirited from the field without having opened his mouth once. Thus he did not jeopardize the dignity of his first reception, a reception illumined by the presence of the Secretaries of War and the Navy, Mayor Michael J. Moriarity of New York, the Premier of Canada, Governors Fanniman, Groves, McFeely and Critchfield, and a brilliant array of European diplomats. Smurch did not, in fact, come to in time to take part in the gigantic hullabaloo arranged at City Hall for the next day. He was rushed to a secluded nursing home and confined in bed. It was nine days before he was able to get up, or to be more exact, before he was permitted to get up. Meanwhile the greatest minds in the country, in solemn assembly, had arranged a secret conference of city, state, and government officials, which Smurch was to attend for the purpose of being instructed in the ethics and behavior of heroism.

On the day that the little mechanic was finally allowed to get up and dress and, for the first time in two weeks, took a great chew of tobacco, he was permitted to receive the newspapermen – this by way of testing him out. Smurch did not wait for questions. 'Youse guys,' he said – and the *Times* man winced – 'youse guys can tell the cock-eyed world dat I put it over on Lindbergh, see? Yeh – an' made an ass o' them two frogs.' The 'two frogs' was a reference to a pair of gallant French fliers who, in attempting a flight only halfway round the world, had, two weeks before, unhappily been lost at sea. The *Times* man was bold enough, at this point, to sketch out for Smurch the accepted formula for interviews in cases of this kind; he explained that there should be no arrogant statements belittling the achievements of other heroes, particularly heroes of foreign nations. 'Ah, the hell with that,' said Smurch. 'I did it, see? I did it, an' I'm talkin' about it.' And he did talk about it.

None of this extraordinary interview was, of course, printed. On the contrary, the newspapers, already under the disciplined direction of a secret directorate created for the occasion and composed of statesmen and editors, gave out to a panting and restless world that 'Jacky,' as he had been arbitrarily nicknamed, would consent to say only that he was very happy and that anyone could have done what he did. 'My achievement has been, I fear, slightly exaggerated,' the *Times* man's article had him protest, with a modest smile. These newspaper stories were kept from the hero, a restriction which did not serve to abate the rising malevolence of his temper. The situation was, indeed, extremely grave, for Pal Smurch was, as he kept insisting, 'rarin' to go.' He could not much longer be kept from a nation clamorous to lionize him. It was the most desperate crisis the United

States of America had faced since the sinking of the *Lusitania*.

On the afternoon of the twenty-seventh of July, Smurch was spirited away to a conference-room in which were gathered mayors, governors, government officials, behaviorist psychologists, and editors. He gave them each a limp, moist paw and a brief unlovely grin. 'Hah ya?' he said. When Smurch was seated, the Mayor of New York arose and, with obvious pessimism, attempted to explain what he must say and how he must act when presented to the world, ending his talk with a high tribute to the hero's courage and integrity. The Mayor was followed by Governor Fanniman of New York, who, after a touching declaration of faith, introduced Cameron Spottiswood, Second Secretary of the American Embassy in Paris, the gentleman selected to coach Smurch in the amenities of public ceremonies. Sitting in a chair, with a soiled yellow tie in his hand and his shirt open at the throat, unshaved, smoking a rolled cigarette, Jack Smurch listened with a leer on his lips. 'I get ya, I get ya,' he cut in, nastily. 'Ya want me to ack like a softy, huh? Ya want me to ack like that —— —— baby-face Lindbergh, huh? Well, nuts to that, see?' Everyone took in his breath sharply; it was a sigh and a hiss. 'Mr Lindbergh,' began a United States Senator, purple with rage, 'and Mr Byrd—' Smurch, who was paring his nails with a jackknife, cut in again. 'Byrd!' he exclaimed. 'Aw fa God's sake, *dat* big—' Somebody shut off his blasphemies with a sharp word. A newcomer had entered the room. Everyone stood up, except Smurch, who, still busy with his nails did not even glance up. 'Mr Smurch,' said someone, sternly, 'the President of the United States!' It had been thought that the presence of the Chief Executive might have a chastening effect upon the young hero, and the former had been, thanks to the remarkable cooperation of the press, secretly brought to the obscure conference-room.

A great, painful silence fell. Smurch looked up, waved a hand at the President. 'How ya comin'?' he asked, and began rolling a fresh cigarette. The silence deepened. Someone coughed in a strained way. 'Geez, it's hot, ain't it?' said Smurch. He loosened two more shirt buttons, revealing a hairy chest and the tattooed word 'Sadie' enclosed in a stencilled heart. The great and important men in the room, faced by the most serious crisis in recent American history, exchanged worried frowns. Nobody seemed to know how to proceed. 'Come awn, come awn,' said Smurch. 'Let's get the hell out of here! When do I start cuttin' in on de parties, huh? And what's they goin' to be *in* it?' He rubbed a thumb and forefinger together meaningly. 'Money!' exclaimed a state senator, shocked, pale. 'Yeh, money,' said Pal, flipping his cigarette out of a window. 'An' big money.' He began rolling a fresh cigarette. 'Big money,' he repeated, frowning over the rice paper. He tilted back in his chair, and leered at each gentleman, separately, the leer of an animal that knows its power, the leer of a leopard loose in a bird-and-dog shop. 'Aw fa God's sake, let's get some place where it's cooler,' he said. 'I been cooped up plenty for three weeks!'

Smurch stood up and walked over to an open window, where he stood staring down into the street, nine floors below. The faint shouting of newsboys floated up to him. He made out his name. 'Hot dog!' he cried, grinning, ecstatic. He leaned out over the still. 'You tell 'em, babies!' he shouted down. 'Hot diggity dog!' In the tense little knot of men standing behind him, a quick, mad impulse flared up. An unspoken word of appeal, of command, seemed to ring through the room. Yet it was deadly silent. Charles K. L. Brand, secretary to the Mayor of New York City, happened to be standing nearest Smurch; he looked inquiringly at the President of the United States. The President, pale, grim, nodded shortly. Brand, a tall, powerfully built man, once a tackle at Rutgers, stepped forward, seized the greatest man in the world by his left shoulder and the seat of his pants, and pushed him out the window.

'My God, he's fallen out the window!' cried a quick-witted editor.

'Get me out of here!' cried the President. Several men sprang to his side and he was hurriedly escorted out of a door toward a side-entrance of the building. The editor of the Associated Press took charge, being used to such things. Crisply he ordered certain men to leave, others to stay; quickly he outlined a story which all the papers were to agree on, sent two men to the street to handle that end of the tragedy, commanded a Senator to sob and two Congressmen to go to pieces nervously. In a word, he skillfully set the stage for the gigantic task that was to follow, the task of breaking to a grief-stricken world the sad story of the untimely, accidental death of its most illustrious and spectacular figure.

The funeral was, as you know, the most elaborate, the

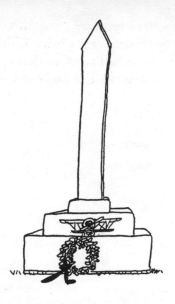

finest, the solemnest, and the saddest ever held in the United States of America. The monument in Arlington Cemetery, with its clean white shaft of marble and the simple device of a tiny plane carved on its base, is a place for pilgrims, in deep reverence, to visit. The nations of the world paid lofty tributes to little Jacky Smurch, America's greatest hero. At a given hour there were two minutes of silence throughout the nation. Even the inhabitants of the small, bewildered town of Westfield, Iowa, observed the touching ceremony; agents of the Department of Justice saw to that. One of them was especially assigned to stand grimly in the doorway of a little shack restaurant on the edge of the tourists' camping ground just outside the town.

There, under his stern scrutiny, Mrs Emma Smurch bowed her head above two hamburger steaks sizzling on her grill – bowed her head and turned away, so that the Secret Service man could not see the twisted, strangely familiar, leer on her lips.

'Yoo-hoo, It's Me and the Ape Man'

'You Wait Here and I'll Bring the Etchings Down'

'Well, Who Made the Magic Go out of Our Marriage
– You or Me?'

'Have You Seen My Pistol, Honey-Bun?'

'What Have You Done with Dr. Millmoss?'

'All, Right, All Right, Try it That Way!
Go Ahead and Try it That Way!'

'Well, it Makes a Difference to *Me*!'

'You said a moment ago that everybody you look at
seems to be a rabbit. Now just what do you mean
by that, Mrs. Sprague?

'For the last time, you and your horsie get away
from me and stay away!'

'That's my first wife up there, and this is the
present Mrs. Harris.'

'All right, have it your way – you heard a seal bark.'

'I wouldn't rent this room to everybody, Mr Spencer.
This is where my husand lost his mind.'

'Darling, I seem to have this rabbit'

'I don't know them either, dear, but there may be
some very simple explanation.'

'If you can keep a secret, I'll tell you how
my husband died.'

'Well, if I called the wrong number, why did you answer the phone?'

'Now I'm going to go in over you horns!'

'Perhaps *this* will refresh your memory.'

'I brought a couple of midgets – do you mind?'

'This gentleman was kind enough to see me home,
darling.'

'Have You People Got Any .38 Cartridges?'

'I'm Helping Mr Gorley with His Novel, Darling'

'It's Lida Bascom's husband – he's frightfully unhappy.'

'Stop Me!'

'I Don't Know. George Got It Somewhere'

'I can't get in touch with your uncle, but there's
a horse here that wants to say hallo'

Nine Needles

ONE OF the more spectacular minor happenings of the past few years which I am sorry that I missed took place in the Columbus, Ohio, home of some friends of a friend of mine. It seems that a Mr Albatross, while looking for something in his medicine cabinet one morning, discovered a bottle of a kind of patent medicine which his wife had been taking for a stomach ailment. Now, Mr Albatross is one of those apprehensive men who are afraid of patent medicines and of almost everything else. Some weeks before, he had encountered a paragraph in a Consumers' Research bulletin which announced that this particular medicine was bad for you. He had thereupon ordered his wife to throw out what was left of her supply of the stuff and never buy any more. She had promised, and here now was another bottle of the perilous liquid. Mr Albatross, a man given to quick rages, shouted the conclusion of the story at my friend: 'I threw the bottle out the bathroom window and the medicine chest after it!' It seems to me that must have been a spectacle worth going a long way to see.

I am sure that many a husband has wanted to wrench the family medicine cabinet off the wall and throw it out the window, if only because the average medicine cabinet is so

"'And the Medicine Chest After It!'"

filled with mysterious bottles and unidentifiable objects of all kinds that it is a source of constant bewilderment and exasperation to the American male. Surely the British medicine cabinet and the French medicine cabinet and all the other medicine cabinets must be simpler and better ordered than ours. It may be that the American habit of saving everything and never throwing anything away, even empty bottles, causes the domestic medicine cabinet to become as cluttered in its small way as the American attic becomes cluttered in its major way. I have encountered few medicine cabinets in this country which were not pack-jammed with something between a hundred and fifty and two hundred different items, from dental floss to boracic acid, from razor blades to sodium perborate, from adhesive tape to coconut oil. Even the neatest wife will put off clearing out the medicine cabinet on the ground that she has something else to do that is more important at the moment, or more diverting. It was in the apartment of such a wife and her husband that I became enormously involved with a medicine cabinet one morning not long ago.

I had spent the weekend with this couple – they live on East Tenth Street near Fifth Avenue – such a weekend as left me reluctant to rise up on Monday morning with bright and shining face and go to work. They got up and went to work, but I didn't. I didn't get up until about two-thirty in the afternoon. I had my face all lathered for shaving and the washbowl was full of hot water when suddenly I cut myself with the razor. I cut my ear. Very few men cut their ears with razors, but I do, possibly because I was taught the old Spencerian free-wrist movement by my writing teacher in the grammar grades. The ear bleeds rather profusely when cut with a razor and is difficult to get at. More angry than hurt, I jerked open the door of the medicine cabinet to see if I could find a styptic pencil and out fell, from the top shelf, a little black paper packet containing nine needles. It seems that this wife kept a little paper packet containing nine needles on the top shelf of the medicine cabinet. The packet fell into the soapy water of the washbowl, where the paper rapidly disintegrated, leaving nine needles at large in the bowl. I was, naturally enough, not in the best condition, either physical or mental, to recover nine needles from a washbowl. No gentleman who has lather on his face and whose ear is bleeding is in the best condition for anything, even something involving the handling of nine large blunt objects.

It did not seem wise to me to pull the plug out of the washbowl and let the needles go down the drain. I had visions of clogging up the plumbing system of the house, and also a vague fear of causing short circuits somehow or other (I know very little about electricity and I don't want to have it explained to me). Finally, I groped very gently around the bowl and eventually has four of the needles in the palm of one hand and three in the palm of the other – two I couldn't find. If I had thought quickly and clearly, I wouldn't have done that. A lathered man whose ear is bleeding and who had four wet needles in one hand and three in the other may be said to have reached the lowest known point of human efficiency. There is nothing he can do but stand there. I tried transferring the needles in my left hand to the palm of my right hand, but I couldn't get them off my left hand. Wet needles cling to you. In the end, I wiped the needles off on to a bathtowel which was hanging on a rod above the bathtub. It was the only towel that I could find. I had to dry my hands afterward on the bathmat. Then I tried to find the needles in the towel. Hunting for seven needles in a bathtowel is the most tedious occupation I have ever engaged in. I could find only five of them. With the two that had been left in the bowl, that meant there were four needles in all missing – two in the washbowl and two others lurking in the towel or lying in the bathtub under the towel. Frightful thoughts came to me of what might happen to anyone who used that towel or washed his face in the bowl or got into the tub, if I didn't find the missing needles. Well, I didn't find them. I sat down on the edge of the tub to think, and I decided finally that the only thing to do was wrap up the towel in a newspaper and take it away with me. I also decided to leave a note for my friends explaining as clearly as I could that I was afraid there were two needles in the bathtub and two needles in the washbowl, and that they better be careful.

I looked everywhere in the apartment, but I could not find a pencil, or a pen, or a typewriter. I could find pieces of paper, but nothing with which to write on them. I don't know what gave me the idea – a movie I had seen, perhaps, or a story I had read – but I suddenly thought of writing a message with a lipstick. The wife might have an extra lipstick lying around and, if so, I concluded it would be in the medicine cabinet. I went back to the medicine cabinet and began poking around in it for a lipstick. I saw what I thought looked like the metal tip of one, and I got two fingers around and it and began to pull gently – it was under a lot of things. Every object in the medicine cabinet began to slide. Bottles broke in the washbowl and on the floor; red, brown, and white liquids spurted; nail files, scissors, razor blades, and miscellaneous objects sang and clattered and tinkled. I was covered with perfume, peroxide, and cold cream.

It took me half an hour to get the debris all together in the middle of the bathroom floor. I made no attempt to put anything back in the medicine cabinet. I knew it would take a steadier hand than mine and a less shattered spirit. Before I went away (only partly shaved) and abandoned the shambles, I left a note saying that I was afraid there were needles in the bathtub and the washbowl and that I had taken their towel and that I would call up and tell them everything – I wrote it in iodine with the end of a toothbrush. I have not yet called up, I am sorry to say. I have neither found the courage nor thought up the words to explain what happened. I suppose my friends believe that I deliberately smashed up their bathroom and stole their towel. I don't know for sure, because they have not yet called me up, either.

Remembrance of
Things Past

I READ the other day about some chickens that got drunk on mash; out in Iowa, I believe it was. I was reminded of the last chickens that I got drunk. They belonged to a French woman who owned a farm in Normandy, near Granville, where I stayed from early spring until late autumn, ten years ago. The drunken chickens make as good a point of beginning as any for the recollections of Madame Goriaut, who owned the farm. I feel that I owe her some small memoir.

I recall the little farmhouse clearly. I saw it first in a slanting rain, as I walked past sheep meadows in which poppies were blooming. A garrulous, tall old man with a blowing white beard walked with me to the farm. He dealt in clocks and watches and real estate, and it was in his dim, ticking shop in the village of Cassis that I had heard of Madame Goriaut's and the room on the second floor which she rented out when she could. I think he went along to be sure that he would get his commission for directing me there.

The room was long and high and musty, with a big, soft bed, and windows that looked out on the courtyard of the place. It was like a courtyard, anyway, in form and in feeling. It should have held old wagon wheels and busy men

in leather aprons, but the activity I remember was that of several black-and-white kittens stalking each other in a circular bed of red geraniums, which, of course, is not like a courtyard, but nevertheless I remember the space in front of the house as being like a courtyard. A courtyard, let us say, with black-and-white kittens stalking each other in a circular bed of red geraniums.

The kittens were wild and unapproachable. Perhaps the fear of man had been struck into their hearts by Madame Goriaut. She was a formidable woman, almost, in a way, *épouvantable* (*épouvantable* was her favorite word – everything was *épouvantable*: the miserable straw crop, the storms off the Channel, the state of the nation, America's delay in getting into the War). Madame was large and shapeless and possessed of an unforgettable toothiness. Her smile, under her considerable mustache, was quick and savage and frightening, like a flash of lightning lighting up a ruined woods. Whether she was tremendously amused (as by the fidgetings of a hanging rabbit – they hang rabbits for the table in Normandy) or tremendously angry (as over the

145

breaking of a crock by her sulky little daughter) you could not determine by her expression. She raised her upper lip and showed her teeth and bellowed, in anger as well as in gaiety. You could identify her moods only by her roaring words, which reverberated around the house like the reports of shotguns. There was no mid-point in her spirit: she was either greatly pleased, usually about nothing much, or greatly displeased, by very little more.

Like many French people in the provinces, Madame Goriaut believed that all Americans were rich. She would ask me if I had not paid a thousand francs for my shoes. My spectacle rims were of solid gold, to be sure. I carried – was it not so? – a thousand dollars in my pockets for tobacco and odds and ends. I would turn my pockets inside out to show her this was not true. At these times she frightened me. It was not too fantastic to conceive of Madame Goriaut creeping into one's room at night with a kitchen knife and a basket, come to pluck one's thousand dollars and one's life as she might pluck spinach. I was always slightly alarmed by her. She had but little English – 'I love you,' 'kiss me,' 'thousand dollars,' 'no,' and 'yes.' I don't know where she learned these words, but she enjoyed repeating them, in that order, and with heavy delight, like a child who has learned a poem. Sometimes she gave me the shudders saying, *apropos* of nothing at all, 'I love you, kiss me, thousand dollars, no, yes.'

Madame Goriaut was a widow. Her husband had been a great professor, she told me. He had died a few years before, leaving her the farm, no money, and two five-act plays in blank verse. She showed the plays to me the first day I was there. They were written in ink in a fine hand, I picked them up and put them down with an imitation of awed pleasure. I wondered what her husband could have been like, the great professor. I found out a little now and then. Once I asked her if she had a photograph of him and she said no, because he had believed that in the transference of one's image to a film or plate there departed a certain measure of one's substance. Did I believe this was true? I said I did indeed. I was afraid to refute any of the convictions of the great professor when madame put them to me with her leer and her fierce, sudden laugh. Of these convictions the only other I remember is that M. Goriaut believed he would come back after death as a *hirondelle*, or swallow. There were a lot of swallows around the farmhouse and the barns, and Madame Goriaut asked me if I thought that one of them was her husband. I asked her, in turn, if any of the swallows had ever made her a sign. She bellowed with laughter. I couldn't tell much about that laugh. I couldn't tell what she had thought of her husband alive, or what she believed of him dead.

I got chickens drunk one Sunday morning by throwing to them pieces of bread soaked in Calvados, strong, new Calvados. Madame had invaded my room one Saturday night after dinner to ask me again why America had got into the War so late. She was bitter on that subject. While she talked she noticed that I had a bottle of Bénédictine on my desk. She said that Bénédictine was not the thing; I must have Calvados, the grand *eau de vie* of the region; she would give me a bottle of it. She went downstairs and brought it up to me, a large bottle. '*Voilà!*' she roared, plonking it down on the table. I thanked her. Later she charged me seven francs for it on my weekly bill. I couldn't drink the stuff, it was so green and violent, so I fed it to the chickens. They got very drunk and fell down and got up and fell down again. Madame did not know what was the matter, and she raged around the village about a new disease that had come to kill the chickens and to impoverish her. The chickens were all right by Monday morning – that is, physically. Mentally, I suppose, it was their worst day.

Once I went with Madame Goriaut and her daughter, who was about seven but was peaked and whiny and looked twelve, to a village fair in Cassis. The little girl led the family donkey by his halter. It turned out when we got there that they were going to offer the donkey for sale; it seems that they offered him for sale every year at the fair. Madame hung a little sign around his neck saying that he was for sale; she had carried the sign to the fair wrapped in a newspaper. Nobody bought the donkey, but one man stepped up and asked how old he was. The little girl replied, 'Twelve years!' Madame Goriaut flew into one of her rages and cuffed the child to the ground with the back of her hand. 'But he has only eight years, monsieur!' she bellowed at the man, who was moving away. She followed him, bellowing, but he evaded her and she returned, still bellowing. She told me later that the donkey was twenty-four years old. Her daughter, she said, would make some man a miserable wife one day.

After the fair we went to a three-table *terrasse* on a narrow pavement in front of a tawdry café in the village and she ordered Calvados. There was, I noticed, a small insect in my glass when it was set in front of me. I called to the waiter, but he had gone back into the café and didn't hear me. Madame asked what was the matter, and I showed her the insect in the bottom of the glass. She shrugged, said '*Ah, là!*' and exchanged glasses with me. She drank the insect placidly. When I paid for the drinks, I brought out a new five-franc note. The little girl's eyes widened and she grabbed for it. '*Quel joli billet de cinq francs!*' she squealed. Her mother slapped her down again, shouting that the *joli billet* belonged to monsieur, who was a wealthy gentleman unused to *épouvantables* children. The little girl cried sullenly. '*Par exemple!*' cried madame, with her toothy leer. 'But you may make her a small present when you leave us.' We had another drink against the black day when I should leave them.

The day I left a man came for me and my bags in a two-wheeled cart. It was getting on toward November and Normandy was growing chill. A cold rain was falling. I piled my bags in the back of the cart and was about to shake hands with madame when the little girl squealed that I had not given her the present I had promised her. I took a five-franc note from my bill-fold and handed it to her. She grabbed it and ran, screaming in delight, a delight that turned to terror as madame, bellowing her loudest, set off in pursuit. They disappeared around a corner of the house, and I could hear them screaming and bellowing in the orchard behind the house. I climbed into the cart and told the man to drive on. He said it was always like that with the young ones nowadays, they wanted everything for themselves. I was gone long before madame came back, as I suppose she did, to say good-bye. I couldn't have faced her.

Better to Have Loafed and Lost

I sometimes wonder about the little girl. She must be seventeen by now, and is probably already making some man a miserable wife.

What are the Leftists Saying?

FOR A long time I have had the idea that it would be interesting to attempt to explain to an average worker what the leftist, or socially conscious, literary critics are trying to say. Since these critics are essentially concerned with the improvement of the worker's status, it seems fitting and proper that the worker should be educated in the meaning of their pronouncements. The critics themselves believe, of course, in the education of the worker, but they are divided into two schools about it: those who believe the worker should be taught beforehand why there must be a revolution, and those who believe that he should be taught afterwards why there was one. This is but one of many two-school systems which divide the leftist intellectuals and keep them so busy in controversy that the worker is pretty much left out of things. It is my plan to escort a worker to a hypothetical, but typical, gathering of leftist literary critics and interpret for him, in so far as I can, what is being said there. The worker is likely to be so confused at first, and so neglected, that he will want to slip out and go to Minsky's; but it is important that he stay, and I hope that he has already taken a chair and removed his hat. I shall sit beside him and try to clarify what is going on.

Nothing, I must explain while we are waiting for the gentlemen to gather, is going to be easy. This is partly because it is a primary tenet of leftist criticism to avoid what is known as Oversimplification. This is a word our worker is going to encounter frequently at the gathering of critics and it is important that he understands what it means. Let me get at it by quoting a sentence from a recent review in *The Nation* by a socially conscious critic: 'In so far as men assert and counter-assert, you can draw an assertion from the comparison of their assertions.' As it stands that is not oversimplified, because no one can point to any exact or absolute meaning it has. Now I will oversimplify it. A says, 'Babe Ruth is dead' (assertion). B says, 'Babe Ruth is alive' (counter-assertion). C says 'You guys seem to disagree' (assertion drawn from comparison of assertions). Here I have brought the critic's sentence down to a definite meaning by providing a concrete instance. Leftist criticism does not believe in that, contending that all thought is in a state of motion, and that in every thought there exists simultaneously 'being,' 'non-being,' and 'becoming,' and that in the end every thought disappears by being absorbed into its opposite. I am afraid that I am oversimplifying again.

Let us get back to our meeting. About sixteen leftist literary critics have now gathered in the room. Several are talking and the others are not so much listening as waiting for an opening. Let us cock an ear toward Mr Hubert Camberwell. Mr Camberwell is saying, 'Sinclair Lewis has dramatized the process of disintegration, as well as his own dilemma, in the outlines of his novels, in the progress of his characters, and sometimes, and most painfully, in the

'The others are not so much listening as waiting
for an opening'

lapses of taste and precision that periodically weaken the structure of his prose.' This is a typical leftist critic's sentence. It has a facile, portentous swing, it damns a prominent author to hell, and it covers a tremendous amount of ground. It also has an air of authority, and because of this the other critics will attack it. Up speaks a Mr Scholzweig: 'But you cannot, with lapses of any kind, *dramatize* a process, you can only *annotate* it.' This is a minor criticism at best, but it is the only one Mr Scholzweig can think of, because he agrees in general with what has been said about Sinclair Lewis (whose books he has never been able to read). At this point Donald Crowley announces that as yet nobody has *defined* anything; that is, nobody had defined 'lapses,' 'dramatize,' 'process,' or 'annotate.' While a small, excited man in shell-rim glasses is asking how he would define the word 'definition' in a world of flux, let us listen to Mr Herman Bernheim. Mr Bernheim is muttering something about Camberwell's 'methodology' and his failure to 'implement' his argument. Now, 'methodology' as the leftist intellectuals use it, means any given wrong method of approach to a subject. 'To implement' means (1) to have at the tip of one's tongue everything that has been written by any leftist since Marx, for the purpose of denying it, and (2) to possess and make use of historical references that begin like this: 'Because of the more solidly articulated structure of French society, the deep-seated sentiments and prejudices of the northern French, and the greater geographical and political accessibility of France to the propaganda of the counter-Reformation,' etc.

The critics have by this time got pretty far away from Camberwell's analysis of Sinclair Lewis, but this is the old customary procedure when leftists begin refuting one another's statements, and is one phase of what is known as 'dialectic.' Dialectic, in this instance, means the process of discriminating one's own truth from the other person's error. This leads to 'factionalism,' another word our worker must be familiar with. Factionalism is that process of disputation by means of which the main point at issue is lost sight of. Now, the main point at issue here – namely, the analysis of Sinclair Lewis – becomes even more blurred by the fact that a critic named Kyle Forsythe, who has just come into the room, gets the erroneous notion that everybody is discussing Upton Sinclair. He begins, although it is not at all relevant, to talk about 'escapism.' Escapism means the activities of anyone who is not a leftist critic or writer. The discussion, to our worker, will now appear to get so far out of hand that we must bring him a Scotch-and-soda if we are to hold his interest much longer. He will probably want to know whether one leftist intellectual ever agrees with another, and, under cover of the loud talking, I shall explain the one form of agreement which these critics have. I call it the 'that he – but when' form of agreement. Let us say that one leftist critic writes in a liberal weekly as follows: 'I like poetry, but I don't like Tennyson.' Another leftist critic will write often in the same issue and immediately following the first one's article: 'That he likes poetry, we must concede Mr Blank, but when he says that Tennyson is a great poet, we can only conclude that he does not like poetry at all.' This is, of course, greatly oversimplified.

Midnight eventually arrives at our party and everybody begins 'unmasking' everybody else's 'ideology.' To explain what unmasking an ideology means, I must give an example. Suppose that I were to say to one of the critics at this party, 'My country, 'tis of thee, sweet land of liberty.' He would unmask my ideology – that is expose the background of my illusion – by pointing out that I am the son of wealthy bourgeois parents who employed an English butler. This is not true, but my ideology would be unmasked, anyway. It is interesting to note that it takes only one leftist critic to expose anybody's ideology, and that every leftist critic unmasks ideologies in his own special way. In this sense, Marxist criticism is very similar to psychoanalysis. Ideology-unmasking is a great deal like dream interpretation and leads to just as many mystic results.

A general midnight unmasking of ideologies at a gathering of leftist literary critics is pretty exciting, and I hope that a second Scotch-and-soda will persuade our worker to stay. If he does, he will find out that when your ideology is unmasked, you can't do anything with it, because it has no 'social currency.' In other words, anything that you say or do will have no more validity than Confederate money.

The party now breaks up, without ill feeling, because the critics have all had such a good time at the unmasking. A leftist critic gets as much fun out of disputation, denial, and disparagement as a spaniel puppy gets out of a steak bone. Each one will leave, confident that he has put each of the others in his place and that they realize it. This is known as the 'united front.' On our way out, however, I must explain to the worker the meaning of an extremely important term in Marxist criticism: namely 'Dialectical Materialism.' Dialectical Materialism, then, is based on two fundamental laws of dialectics: the law of the permeation of opposites, or polar unity, and the law of the negation of the negation, or development through opposites. This second proposition is the basic law of all processes of thought. I will first state the law itself and then support it with examples – Hey, worker! Wait for baby!

The Little Girl and the Wolf

ONE AFTERNOON a big wolf waited in a dark forest for a little girl to come along carrying a basket of food to her grandmother. Finally a little girl did come along and she was carrying a basket of food. 'Are you carrying that basket to your grandmother?' asked the wolf. The little girl said yes, she was. So the wolf asked her where her grandmother lived and the little girl told him and he disappeared into the wood.

When the little girl opened the door of her grandmother's house she saw that there was somebody in bed with a nightcap and nightgown on. She had approached no nearer than twenty-five feet from the bed when she saw that it was not her grandmother but the wolf, for even in a nightcap a wolf does not look any more like your grandmother than the Metro-Goldwyn lion looks like Calvin Coolidge. So the little girl took an automatic out of her basket and shot the wolf dead.

Moral: It is not so easy to fool little girls nowadays as it used to be.

Courtship Through the Ages

SURELY NOTHING in the astonishing scheme of life can have nonplussed Nature so much as the fact that none of the females of any of the species she created really cared very much for the male, as such. For the past ten million years Nature has been busily inventing ways to make the male attractive to the female, but the whole business of courtship, from the marine annelids up to man, still lumbers heavily along, like a complicated musical comedy. I have been reading the sad and absorbing story in Volume 6 (Cole to Dama) of the Encyclopaedia Britannica. In this volume you can learn about cricket, cotton, costume designing, crocodiles, crown jewels, and Coleridge, but none of these subjects is so interesting as the Courtship of Animals, which recounts the sorrowful lengths to which all males must go to arouse the interest of a lady.

We all know, I think, that Nature gave man whiskers and a mustache with the quaint idea in mind that these would prove attractive to the female. We all know that, far from attracting her, whiskers and mustaches only made her nervous and gloomy, so that man had to go in for somersaults, tilting with lances, and performing feats of parlor magic to win her attention; he also had to bring her candy, flowers, and the furs of animals. It is common knowledge that in spite of all these 'love displays' the male is constantly being turned down, insulted, or thrown out of the house. It is rather comforting, then, to discover that the peacock, for all his gorgeous plumage, does not have a particularly easy time in courtship; none of the males in the world do. The first peahen, it turned out, was only faintly stirred by her suitor's beautiful train. She would often go quietly to sleep while he was whisking it around. The Britannica tells us that the peacock actually had to learn a certain little trick to wake her up and revive her interest: he had to learn to vibrate his quills so as to make a rustling sound. In ancient times man himself, observing the ways of the peacock, probably tried vibrating his whiskers to make a rustling sound; if so, it didn't get him anywhere. He had to go in for something else; so, among other things, he went in for gifts. It is not unlikely that he got his idea from certain flies and birds who were making no headway at all with rustling sounds.

One of the flies of the family Empidae, who had tried everything, finally hit on something pretty special. He contrived to make a glistening transparent balloon which was even larger than himself. Into this he would put sweet-meats and tidbits and he would carry the whole elaborate envelope through the air to the lady of his choice. This amused her for some time, but she finally got bored with it. She demanded silly little colorful presents, something that you couldn't eat but that would look nice around the house. So the male Empis had to go around gathering flower petals and pieces of bright paper to put into his balloon. On a courtship flight a male Empis cuts quite a figure now, but he can hardly be said to be happy. He never knows how soon the female will demand heavier presents, such as Roman coins and gold collar buttons. It seems probable that one day the courtship of the Empidae will fall down, as man's occasionally does, of it own weight.

The bowerbird is another creature that spends so much time courting the female that he never gets any work done. If all the male bowerbirds became nervous wrecks within the next ten or fifteen years, it would not surprise me. The female bowerbird insists that a playground be built for her with a specially constructed bower at the entrance. This bower is much more elaborate than an ordinary nest and is harder to build; it costs a lot more, too. The female will not come into the playground until the male has filled it up with a great many gifts: silvery leaves, red leaves, rose petals, shells, beads, berries, bones, dice, buttons, cigar bands, Christmas seals, and the Lord knows what else. When the female finally condescends to visit the playground, she is in a coy and silly mood and has to be chased in and out of the bower and up and down the playground before she will quit giggling and stand still long enough even to shake hands. The male bird is, of course, pretty well done in before the chase starts, because he has worn himself out hunting for eyeglass lenses and begonia blossoms. I imagine that many a bowerbird, after chasing a female for two or three hours, says the hell with it and goes home to bed. Next day, of course, he telephones someone else and the same trying ritual is gone through with again. A male bowerbird is as exhausted as a night-club habitué before he is out of his twenties.

The male fiddler crab has a somewhat easier time, but it can hardly be said that he is sitting pretty. He has one enormously large and powerful claw, usually brilliantly colored, and you might suppose that all he had to do was reach out and grab some passing cutie. The very earliest fiddler crabs may have tried this, but, if so, they got slapped for their pains. A female fiddler crab will not tolerate any cave-man stuff; she never has and she doesn't intend to start now. To attract a female, a fiddler crab has to stand on tiptoe and brandish his claw in the air. If any female in the neighborhood is interested – and you'd be surprised how many are not – she comes over and engages him in light badinage, for which he is not in the mood. As many as a hundred females may pass the time of day with him and go on about their business. By nightfall of an average courting day, a fiddler crab who has been standing on tiptoe for eight or ten hours waving a heavy claw in the air is in pretty sad shape. As in the case of the males of all species, however, he gets out of bed next morning, dashes some water on his face, and tries again.

The next time you encounter a male web-spinning spider, stop and reflect that he is too busy worrying about his love life to have any desire to bite you. Male web-spinning spiders have a tougher life than any other males in the animal kingdom. This is because the female web-spinning spiders have very poor eyesight. If a male lands on a female's web, she kills him before he has time to lay down his cane and gloves, mistaking him for a fly or a bumblebee who has stumbled into her trap. Before the species figured out what to do about this, millions of males were murdered by ladies they called on. It is the nature of spiders to perform a little dance in front of the female, but before a male spinner could get near enough for the female to see who he was and what he was up to, she would lash out at him with a flat-iron or a pair of garden shears. One night, nobody knows when, a very bright male spinner lay awake worrying about calling on a lady who had been killing suitors right and left. It came to him that this business of dancing as a love display wasn't getting anybody anywhere except the grave. He decided to go in for web-twitching, or strand-vibrating. The next day he tried it on one of the nearsighted girls. Instead of dropping in on her suddenly, he stayed outside the web and began monkeying with one of its strands. He twitched it up and down and in and out with such a lilting rhythm that the female was charmed. The serenade worked beautifully; the female let him live. The Britannica's spider-watchers, however, report that this system is not always successful. Once in a while, even now, a female will fire three bullets into a suitor or run him through with a kitchen knife. She keeps threatening him from the moment he strikes the first low notes on the outside strings, but usually by the time he has got up to the high notes played around the center of the web, he is going to town and she spares his life.

Even the butterfly, as handsome a fellow as he is, can't always win a mate merely by fluttering around and showing off. Many butterflies have to have scent scales on their wings. Hepialus carries a powder puff in a perfumed pouch. He throws perfume at the ladies when they pass. The male tree cricket, Oecanthus, goes Hepialus one better by carrying a tiny bottle of wine with him and giving drinks to such doxies as he has designs on. One of the male snails throws darts to entertain the girls. So it goes, through the long list of animals, from the bristle worm and his rudimentary dance steps to man and his gift of diamonds and sapphires. The golden-eye drake raises a jet of water with his feet as he flies over a lake; Hepialus has his powder puff, Oecanthus his wine bottle, man his etchings. It is a bright and melancholy story, the age-old desire of the male for the female, the age-old desire of the female to be amused and entertained. Of all the creatures on earth, the only males who could be figured as putting any irony into their courtship are the grebes and certain other diving birds. Every now and then a courting grebe slips quietly down to the bottom of the lake and then, with a mighty 'Whoosh!,' pops out suddenly a few feet from his girl friend, splashing water all over her. She seems to be persuaded that this is a purely loving display, but I like to think that the grebe always has a faint hope of drowning her or scaring her to death.

I will close this investigation into the mournful burdens of the male with the Britannica's story about a certain Argus pheasant. It appears that the Argus displays himself in front of a female who stands perfectly still without moving a feather. (If you saw 'June Moon' some years ago and remember the scene in which the songwriter sang 'Montana Moon' to his grim and motionless wife, you have some idea what the female Argus probably thinks of her mate's display.) The male Argus the Britannica tells about was confined in a cage with a female of another species, a female who kept moving around, emptying ashtrays and fussing with lampshades all the time the male was showing off his talents. Finally, in disgust, he stalked away and began displaying in front of his water trough. He reminds me of a certain male (Homo sapiens) of my acquaintance who one night after dinner asked his wife to put down her detective magazine so that he could read her a poem of which he was very fond. She sat quietly enough until he was well into the middle of the thing, intoning with great ardor and intensity. Then suddenly there came a sharp, disconcerting *slap!* It turned out that all during the male's display, the female had been intent on a circling mosquito and had finally trapped it between the palms of her hands. The male in this case did not stalk away and display in front of a water trough; he went over to Tim's and had a flock of drinks and recited the poem to the fellas. I am sure

they all told bitter stories of their own about how their displays had been interrupted by females. I am also sure that they all ended up singing 'Honey, Honey, Bless Your Heart.'

The Whip-Poor-Will

THE NIGHT had just begun to get pale around the edges when the whip-poor-will began. Kinstrey, who slept in a back room on the first floor, facing the meadow and the strip of woods beyond, heard a blind man tapping and a bugle calling and a woman screaming 'Help! Police!' The sergeant in gray was cutting open envelopes with a sword. 'Sit down there, sit down there, sit down there!' he chanted at Kinstrey. 'Sit down there, cut your throat, cut your throat, whip-poor-will, whip-poor-will, whip-poor-will!' And Kinstrey woke up.

He opened his eyes, but lay without moving for several minutes, separating the fantastic morning from the sounds and symbols of his dream. There was the palest wash of light in the room. Kinstrey scowled through tousled hair at his wristwatch and saw that it was ten minutes past four. 'Whip-poor-will, whip-poor-will, whip-poor-will!' The bird sounded very near – in the grass outside the window, perhaps. Kinstrey got up and went to the window in his bare feet and looked out. You couldn't tell where the thing was. The sound was all around you, incredibly loud and compelling and penetrating. Kinstrey had never heard a whip-poor-will so near at hand before. He had heard them as a boy in Ohio in the country, but he remembered their call as faint and plaintive and faraway, dying before long somewhere between the hills and horizon. You didn't hear the bird often in Ohio, it came back to him, and it almost never ventured as close to a house or barn as this brazen-breasted bird murdering sleep out there along the fence line somewhere. 'Whip-poor-will, whip-poor-will, whip-poor-will!' Kinstrey climbed back into bed and began to count; the bird did twenty-seven whips without pausing. His lungs must be built like a pelican's pouch, or a puffin or a penguin or pemmican or a paladin. . . . It was bright daylight when Kinstrey fell asleep again.

At breakfast, Madge Kinstrey, looking cool and well rested in her white piqué house coat, poured the coffee with steady authority. She raised her eyebrows slightly in mild surprise when Kinstrey mentioned the whip-poor-will the second time (she had not listened the first time, for she was lost in exploring with a long, sensitive finger an infinitesimal chip on the rim of her coffee cup).

'Whip-poor-will?' she said, finally. 'No, I didn't hear it. Of course, my room is on the front of the house. You must have been slept out and ready to wake up anyway, or you wouldn't have heard it.'

'Ready to wake up?' said Kinstrey. 'At four o'clock in the morning? I hadn't slept three hours.'

'Well, I didn't hear it,' said Mrs Kinstrey. 'I don't listen for night noises; I don't even hear the crickets or the frogs.'

'Neither do I,' said Kinstrey. 'It's not the same thing. This thing is loud as a fire bell. You can hear it for a mile.'

'I didn't hear it,' she said, buttering a piece of thin toast.

Kinstrey gave it up and turned his scowling attention to the headlines in the *Herald Tribune* of the day before. The vision of his wife sleeping quietly in her canopied four-poster came between his eyes and the ominous headlines. Madge always slept quietly, almost without moving, her arms straight and still outside the covers, her fingers relaxed. She did not believe anyone had to toss and turn. 'It's a notion,' she would tell Kinstrey. 'Don't let your nerves get the best of you. Use your will power.'

'Um, hm,' said Kinstrey aloud, not meaning to.

'Yes, sir?' said Arthur, the Kinstreys' colored butler, offering Kinstrey a plate of hot blueberry muffins.

'Nothing,' said Kinstrey, looking at his wife. 'Did you hear the whip-poor-will, Arthur?'

'No, sir, I didn't,' said Arthur.

'Did Margaret?'

'I don't think she did, sir,' said Arthur. 'She didn't say anything about it.'

The next morning the whip-poor-will began again at the same hour, rolling out its loops and circles of sound across the new day. Kinstrey, in his dreams, was beset by trios of little bearded men rolling hoops at him. He tried to climb up onto a gigantic Ferris wheel whose swinging seats were rumpled beds. The round cop with wheels for feet rolled toward him shouting, 'Will power will, will power will, whip-poor-will!'

Kinstrey opened his eyes and stared at the ceiling and began to count the whips. At one point the bird did fifty-three straight, without pausing. I suppose, like the drops of water or the bright light in the third degree, this could drive you nuts, Kinstrey thought. Or make you confess. He began to think of things he hadn't thought of for years: the time he took the quarter from his mother's pocketbook, the time he steamed open a letter addressed to his father; it was from his teacher in the eighth grade. Miss – let's see – Miss Willpool, Miss Whippoor, Miss Will Power, Miss Wilmott – that was it.

He had reached the indiscretions of his middle twenties when the whip-poor-will suddenly stopped, on 'poor,' not on 'will.' Something must have frightened it. Kinstrey sat up on the edge of the bed and lighted a cigarette and listened. The bird was through calling, all right, but Kinstrey couldn't go back to sleep. The day was as bright as a flag. He got up and dressed.

'I thought you weren't going to smoke cigarettes before breakfast any more,' said Madge later. 'I found four stubs in the ashtray in your bedroom.'

It was no use telling her he had smoked them before going to bed; you couldn't fool Madge; she always knew. 'That goddam bird woke me up again,' he said, 'and this time I couldn't get back to sleep.' He passed her his empty coffee cup. 'It did fifty-three without stopping this morning,' he added. 'I don't know how the hell it breathes.'

His wife took his coffee cup and set it down firmly. 'Not three cups,' she said. 'Not with you sleeping so restlessly the way it is.'

'You didn't hear it, I suppose?' he said.

She poured herself some more coffee. 'No,' she said, 'I didn't hear it.'

Margaret hadn't heard it, either, but Arthur had. Kinstrey talked to them in the kitchen while they were clearing up after breakfast. Arthur said that it 'wuk' him but he went right back to sleep. He said he slept like a log – must be the air off the ocean. As for Margaret, she always slept like a log; only thing ever kept her awake was people a-hoopin' and a-hollerin'. She was glad she didn't hear the whip-poor-will. Down where she came from, she said, if you heard a whip-poor-will singing near the house, it meant there was going to be a death. Arthur said he had heard about that, too; must have been his grandma told him, or somebody.

If a whip-poor-will singing near the house meant death, Kinstrey told them, it wouldn't really make any difference whether you heard it or not. 'It doesn't make any difference whether you see the ladder you're walking under,' he said, lighting a cigarette and watching the effect of his words on Margaret. She turned from putting some plates away, and her eyes widened and rolled a little.

'Mr Kinstrey is just teasin' you, Mag,' said Arthur, who smiled and was not afraid. Thinks he's pretty smart, Kinstrey thought. Just a little bit too smart, maybe. Kinstrey remembered Arthur's way of smiling, almost imperceptibly, at things Mrs Kinstrey sometimes said to her husband when Arthur was just coming into the room or just going out – little things that were none of his business to listen to. Like 'Not three cups of coffee if a bird keeps you awake.' Wasn't that what she had said?

'Is there any more coffee?' he asked, testily. 'Or did you throw it out?' He knew they had thrown it out; breakfast had been over for almost an hour.

'We can make you some fresh,' said Arthur.

'Never mind,' said Kinstrey. 'Just don't be so sure of yourself. There's nothing in life to be sure about.'

When, later in the morning, he started out the gate to walk down to the post office, Madge called to him from an upstairs window. 'Where are you going?' she asked, amiably enough. He frowned up at her. 'To the taxidermist's,' he said, and went on.

He realized, as he walked along in the warm sunshine, that he had made something of a spectacle of himself. Just because he hadn't had enough sleep – or enough coffee. It wasn't his fault, though. It was that infernal bird. He discovered, after a quarter of a mile, that the imperative rhythm of the whip-poor-will's call was running through his mind, but the words of the song were new: fatal bell, fatal bell, fa-tal bell. Now, where had that popped up from? It took him some time to place it; it was a fragment from 'Macbeth.' There was something about the fatal bellman crying in the night. 'The fatal bellman cried the live-long night' – something like that. It was an owl that cried the night Duncan was murdered. Funny thing to call up after all these years; he hadn't read the play since college. It was that fool Margaret, talking about the whip-poor-will and the old superstition that if you hear the whip-poor-will singing near the house, it means there is going to be a death. Here it was 1942, and people still believed in stuff like that.

The next dawn the dream induced by the calling of the whip-poor-will was longer and more tortured – a nightmare filled with dark perils and heavy hopelessness. Kinstrey woke up trying to cry out. He lay there breathing hard and listening to the bird. He began to count: one, two, three, four, five . . .

Then, suddenly, he leaped out of bed and ran to the window and began yelling and pounding on the window-pane and running the blind up and down. He shouted and cursed until his voice got hoarse. The bird kept right on going. He slammed the window down and turned away from it, and there was Arthur in the doorway.

'What is it, Mr Kinstrey?' said Arthur. He was fumbling with the end of a faded old bathrobe and trying to blink the sleep out of his eyes. 'Is anything the matter?'

Kinstrey glared at him. 'Get out of here!' he shouted. 'And put some coffee on. Or get me a brandy or something.'

'I'll put some coffee on,' said Arthur. He went shuffling away in his slippers, still half asleep.

'Well,' said Madge Kinstrey over her coffee cup at breakfast, 'I hope you got your tantrum over and done with this morning. I never heard such a spectacle – squalling like a spoiled brat.'

'You can't hear spectacles,' said Kinstrey, coldly. 'You see them.'

'I'm sure I don't know what you're talking about,' she said.

No, you don't, thought Kinstrey, you never have; never have, nev-er have, nev-er have. Would he ever get that damned rhythm out of his head? It struck him that perhaps Madge had no subconscious. When she lay on her back, her eyes closed; when she got up, they opened, like a doll's. The mechanism of her mind was as simple as a cigarette box; it was either open or it was closed, and there was nothing else, nothing else, nothing else . . .

The whole problem turns on a very neat point, Kinstrey thought as he lay awake that night, drumming on the headboard with his fingers. William James would have been interested in it; Henry, too, probably. I've got to ignore this thing, get adjusted to it, become oblivious of it. I mustn't fight it, I mustn't build it up. If I get to screaming at it, I'll be running across that wet grass out there in my bare feet, charging that bird as if it were a trench full of Germans, throwing rocks at it, giving the Rebel yell or something, for God's sake. No, I mustn't build it up. I'll think of something else every time it pops into my mind. I'll name the Dodger infield to myself, over and over: Camilli, Herman, Reese, Vaughan, Camilli, Herman, Reese . . .

Kinstrey did not succeed in becoming oblivious of the whip-poor-will. Its dawn call pecked away at his dreams like a vulture at a heart. It slowly carved out a recurring nightmare in which Kinstrey was attacked by an umbrella whose handle, when you clutched it, clutched right back, for the umbrella was not an umbrella at all but a raven. Through the gloomy hallways of his mind rang the Thing's dolorous cry: nevermore, nevermore, nevermore, whip-poor-will, whip-poor-will . . .

One day, Kinstrey asked Mr Tetford at the post office if the whip-poor-wills ever went away. Mr Tetford squinted at him. 'Don't look like the sun was brownin' you up none,' he said. 'I don't know as they ever go away. They move around. I like to hear 'em. You get used to 'em.'

'Sure,' said Kinstrey. 'What do people do when they can't get used to them, though – I mean old ladies or sick people?'

'Only one's been bothered was old Miss Purdy. She darn near set fire to the whole island tryin' to burn 'em out of her woods. Shootin' at 'em might drive 'em off, or a body could trap 'em easy enough and let 'em loose somewheres else. But people get used to 'em after a few mornings.'

'Oh, sure,' said Kinstrey. 'Sure.'

That evening in the living room, when Arthur brought in the coffee, Kinstrey's cup cackled idiotically in its saucer when he took it off the tray.

Madge Kinstrey laughed. 'Your hand is shaking like a leaf,' she said.

He drank all his coffee at once and looked up savagely. 'If I could get one good night's sleep, it might help,' he said. 'That damn bird! I'd like to wring its neck.'

'Oh, come, now,' she said, mockingly. 'You wouldn't hurt a fly. Remember the mouse we caught in the Westport house? You took it out in the field and let it go.'

'The trouble with you—' he began, and stopped. He opened the lid of a cigarette box and shut it, opened and shut it again, reflectively. 'As simple as that,' he said.

She dropped her amused smile and spoke shortly. 'You're acting like a child about that silly bird,' she said. 'Worse than a child. I was over at the Barrys' this afternoon. Even their little Ann didn't make such a fuss. A whip-poor-will frightened her the first morning, but now she never notices them.'

'I'm not frightened, for God's sake!' shouted Kinstrey. 'Frightened or brave, asleep or awake, open or shut – you make everything black or white.'

'Well,' she said, 'I like that.'

'I think the bird wakes you up, too,' he said. 'I think it wakes up Arthur and Margaret.'

'And we just pretend it doesn't?' she asked. 'Why on earth should we?'

'Oh, out of some fool notion of superiority, I suppose, out of – I don't know.'

'I'll thank you not to class me with the servants,' she said coldly. He lighted a cigarette and didn't say anything. 'You're being ridiculous and childish,' she said, 'fussing about nothing at all, like an invalid in a wheel chair.' She got up and started from the room.

'Nothing at all,' he said, watching her go.

She turned at the door. 'Ted Barry say's he'll take you on at tennis if your bird hasn't worn you down too much.' She went on up the stairs, and he heard her close the door of her room.

He sat smoking moodily for a long time, and fell to wondering whether the man's wife in 'The Raven' had seen what the man had seen perched on the pallid bust of Pallas just above the chamber door. Probably not, he decided. When he went to bed, he lay awake a long while trying to think of the last line of 'The Raven.' He couldn't get any farther than 'Like a demon that is dreaming,' and this kept running through his head. 'Nuts,' he said at last, aloud, and he had the oddly disturbing feeling that it wasn't he who had spoken but somebody else.

*

Kinstrey was not surprised that Madge was a little girl in pigtails and a play suit. The long gray hospital room was filled with poor men in wheel chairs, running their long sensitive fingers around the rims of empty coffee cups. 'Poor Will, poor Will,' chanted Madge, pointing her finger at him. 'Here are your spectacles, here are your spectacles.' One of the sick men was Arthur, grinning at him, grinning at him and holding him with one hand, so that he was powerless to move his arms or legs. 'Hurt a fly, hurt a fly,' chanted Madge. 'Whip him now, whip him now!' she cried, and she was the umpoor in the high chair beside the court, holding a black umbrella over her head: love thirty, love forty, forty-one, forty-two, forty-three, forty-four. His feet were stuck in the wet concrete on his side of the net and Margaret peered over the net at him, holding a skillet for a racquet. Arthur was pushing him down now, and he was caught in the concrete from head to foot. It was Madge laughing and counting over him: refer-three, refer-four, refer-five, refer-will, repoor-will, whip-poor-will, whip-poor-will . . .

The dream still clung to Kinstrey's mind like a cobweb as he stood in the kitchen in his pajamas and bare feet, wondering what he wanted, what he was looking for. He turned on the cold water in the sink and filled a glass, but only took a sip, and put it down. He left the water running. He opened the breadbox and took out half a loaf wrapped in oiled paper, and pulled open a drawer. He took out the bread knife and then put it back and took out the long, sharp carving knife. He was standing there holding the knife in one hand and the bread in the other when the door to the dining room opened. It was Arthur. 'Who do you do first?' Kinstrey said to him, hoarsely . . . .

The Barrys, on their way to the beach in their station wagon, drove into the driveway between the house and the barn. They were surprised to see that, at a quarter to eleven in the morning, the Kinstrey servants hadn't taken in the milk. The bottle, standing on the small back porch, was hot to Barry's touch. When he couldn't rouse anyone, pounding and calling, he climbed up on the cellar door and looked in the kitchen window. He told his wife sharply to get back in the car. . . .

The local police and the state troopers were in and out of the house all day. It wasn't every morning in the year you got called out on a triple murder and suicide.

It was just getting dark when Troopers Baird and Lennon came out of the front door and walked down to their car, pulled up beside the road in front of the house. Out in back, probably in the little strip of wood there, Lennon figured, a whip-poor-will began to call. Lennon listened a minute.

'You ever hear the old people say a whip-poor-will singing near the house means death?' he asked.

Baird grunted and got in under the wheel. Lennon climbed in beside him. 'Take more'n a whip-poor-will to cause a mess like that,' said Trooper Baird, starting the car.

The Secret Life of Walter Mitty

'WE'RE GOING through!' The Commander's voice was like thin ice breaking. He wore his full-dress uniform, with the heavily braided white cap pulled down rakishly over one cold gray eye. 'We can't make it, sir. It's spoiling for a hurricane, if you ask me.' 'I'm not asking you, Lieutenant Berg,' said the Commander. 'Throw on the power lights! Rev her up to 8,500! We're going through!' The pounding of the cylinders increased: ta-pocketa-pocketa-pocketa-*pocketa-pocketa*. The Commander stared at the ice forming on the pilot window. He walked over and twisted a row of complicated dials. 'Switch on No. 8 auxiliary!' he shouted. 'Switch on No. 8 auxiliary!' repeated Lieutenant Berg. 'Full strength in No. 3 turret!' shouted the Commander. 'Full strength in No. 3 turret!' The crew, bending to their various tasks in the huge, hurtling eight-engined Navy hydroplane, looked at each other and grinned. 'The Old Man'll get us through,' they said to one another. 'The Old Man ain't afraid of Hell!' . . .

'Not so fast! You're driving too fast!' said Mrs Mitty. 'What are you driving so fast for?'

'Hmm?' said Walter Mitty. He looked at his wife, in the seat beside him, with shocked astonishment. She seemed grossly unfamiliar, like a strange woman who had yelled at him in a crowd. 'You were up to fifty-five,' she said. 'You know I don't like to go more than forty. You were up to fifty-five.' Walter Mitty drove on toward Waterbury in silence, the roaring of the SN202 through the worst storm in twenty years of Navy flying fading in the remote, intimate airways of his mind. 'You're tensed up again,' said Mrs Mitty. 'It's one of your days. I wish you'd let Dr Renshaw look you over.'

Walter Mitty stopped the car in front of the building where his wife went to have her hair done. 'Remember to get those overshoes while I'm having my hair done,' she said. 'I don't need overshoes,' said Mitty. She put her mirror back into her bag. 'We've been all through that,' she said, getting out of the car. 'You're not a young man any longer.' He raced the engine a little. 'Why don't you wear your gloves? Have you lost your gloves?' Walter Mitty reached in a pocket and brought out the gloves. He put them on, but after she had turned and gone into the building and he had driven on to a red light, he took them off again. 'Pick it up, brother!' snapped a cop as the light changed, and Mitty hastily pulled on his gloves and lurched ahead. He drove around the streets aimlessly for a time, and then he drove past the hospital on his way to the parking lot.

. . . 'It's the millionaire banker, Wellington McMillan,' said the pretty nurse. 'Yes?' said Walter Mitty, removing his gloves slowly. 'Who has the case?' 'Dr Renshaw and Dr Benbow, but there are two specialists here, Dr Remington from New York and Mr Pritchard-Mitford from London. He flew over.' A door opened down a long, cool corridor and

Dr Renshaw came out. He looked distraught and haggard. 'Hello, Mitty,' he said. 'We're having the devil's own time with McMillan, the millionaire banker and close personal friend of Roosevelt. Obstreosis of the ductal tract. Tertiary. Wish you'd take a look at him.' 'Glad to,' said Mitty.

In the operating room there were whispered introductions: 'Dr Remington, Dr Mitty. Mr Pritchard-Mitford, Dr Mitty.' 'I've read your book on streptothricosis,' said Pritchard-Mitford, shaking hands. 'A brilliant performance, sir.' 'Thank you,' said Walter Mitty. 'Didn't know you were in the States, Mitty,' grumbled Remington. 'Coals to Newcastle, bringing Mitford and me up here for a tertiary.' 'You are very kind,' said Mitty. A huge, complicated machine, connected to the operating table, with many tubes and wires, began at this moment to go pocketa-pocketa-pocketa. 'The new anesthetizer is giving way!' shouted an interne. 'There is no one in the East who knows how to fix it!' 'Quiet, man!' said Mitty, in a low, cool voice. He sprang to the machine, which was now going pocketa-pocketa-queep-pocketa-queep. He began fingering delicately a row of glistening dials. 'Give me a fountain pen!' he snapped. Someone handed him a fountain pen. He pulled a faulty piston out of the machine and inserted the pen in its place. 'That will hold for ten minutes,' he said. 'Get on with the operation.' A nurse hurried over and whispered to Renshaw, and Mitty saw the man turn pale. 'Coreopsis has set in,' said Renshaw nervously. 'If you would take over, Mitty?' Mitty looked at him and at the craven figure of Benbow, who drank, and at the grave, uncertain faces of the two great specialists. 'If you wish,' he said. They slipped a white gown on him; he adjusted a mask and drew on thin gloves; nurses handed him shining . . .

'Back it up, Mac! Look out for that Buick!' Walter Mitty jammed on the brakes. 'Wrong lane, Mac,' said the parking-lot attendant, looking at Mitty closely. 'Gee. Yeh,' muttered Mitty. He began cautiously to back out of the lane marked 'Exit Only.' 'Leave her sit there,' said the attendant. 'I'll put her away.' Mitty got out of the car. 'Hey, better leave the key.' 'Oh,' said Mitty, handing the man the ignition key. The attendant vaulted into the car, backed it up with insolent skill, and put it where it belonged.

They're so damn cocky, thought Walter Mitty, walking along Main Street; they think they know everything. Once he had tried to take his chains off, outside New Milford, and he had got them wound around the axles. A man had had to come out in a wrecking car and unwind them, a young, grinning garageman. Since then Mrs Mitty always made him drive to a garage to have the chains taken off. The next time, he thought, I'll wear my right arm in a sling; they won't grin at me then. I'll have my right arm in a sling and they'll see I couldn't possibly take the chains off myself. He kicked at the slush on the sidewalk. 'Overshoes,' he said to himself, and he began looking for a shoe store.

When he came out into the street again, with the over-shoes in a box under his arm, Walter Mitty began to wonder what the other thing was his wife had told him to get. She had told him twice, before they set out from their house for Waterbury. In a way he hated these weekly trips to town – he was always getting something wrong. Kleenex, he thought, Squibb's, razor blades? No. Toothpaste, toothbrush, bicarbonate, carborundum, initiative and referendum? He gave it up. But she would remember it. 'Where's the what's-its-name?' she would ask. 'Don't tell me you forgot the what's-its-name.' A newsboy went by shouting something about the Waterbury trial.

... 'Perhaps this will refresh your memory.' The District Attorney suddenly thrust a heavy automatic at the quiet figure on the witness stand. 'Have you ever seen this before?' Walter Mitty took the gun and examined it expertly. 'This is my Webley-Vickers 50.80,' he said calmly. An excited buzz ran around the courtroom. The judge rapped for order. 'You are a crack shot with any sort of firearms, I believe?' said the District Attorney, insinuatingly. 'Objection!' shouted Mitty's attorney. 'We have shown that the defendant could not have fired the shot. We have shown that he wore his right arm in a sling on the night of the fourteenth of July.' Walter Mitty raised his hand briefly and the bickering attorneys were stilled. 'With any known make of gun,' he said evenly. 'I could have killed Gregory Fitzhurst at three hundred feet *with my left hand*.' Pandemonium broke loose in the courtroom. A woman's scream rose above the bedlam and suddenly a lovely, dark-haired girl was in Walter Mitty's arms. The District Attorney struck at her savagely. Without rising from his chair, Mitty let the man have it on the point of the chin. 'You miserable cur!' ...

'Puppy biscuit,' said Walter Mitty. He stopped walking and the buildings of Waterbury rose up out of the misty courtroom and surrounded him again. A woman who was passing laughed. 'He said "Puppy biscuit,"' she said to her companion. 'That man said "Puppy biscuit" to himself.' Walter Mitty hurried on. He went into an A. & P., not the first one he came to but a smaller one farther up the street. 'I want some biscuit for small, young dogs,' he said to the clerk. 'Any special brand, sir?' The greatest pistol shot in the world thought a moment. 'It says "Puppies Bark for It" on the box,' said Walter Mitty.

His wife would be through at the hairdresser's in fifteen minutes, Mitty saw in looking at his watch, unless they had trouble drying it; sometimes they had trouble drying it. She didn't like to get to the hotel first; she would want him to be there waiting for her as usual. He found a big leather chair in the lobby, facing a window, and he put the over- shoes and the puppy biscuit on the floor beside it. He picked up an old copy of *Liberty* and sank down into the chair. 'Can Germany Conquer the World Through the Air?' Walter Mitty looked at the pictures of bombing planes and of ruined streets.

. . . 'The cannonading has got the wind up in young Raleigh, sir,' said the sergeant. Captain Mitty looked up at him through tousled hair. 'Get him to bed,' he said wearily. 'With the others. I'll fly alone.' 'But you can't, sir,' said the sergeant anxiously. 'It takes two men to handle that bomber and the Archies are pounding hell out of the air. Von Richtman's circus is between here and Saulier.' 'Somebody's got to get that ammunition dump,' said Mitty. 'I'm going over. Spot of brandy?' He poured a drink for the sergeant and one for himself. War thundered and whined around the dugout and battered at the door. There was a rending of wood and splinters flew through the room. 'A bit of a near thing,' said Captain Mitty carelessly. 'The box barrage is closing in,' said the sergeant. 'We only live once, Sergeant,' said Mitty, with his faint, fleeting smile. 'Or do we?' He poured another brandy and tossed it off. 'I never see a man could hold his brandy like you, sir,' said the sergeant. 'Begging your pardon, sir.' Captain Mitty stood up and strapped on his huge Webley-Vickers automatic. 'It's forty kilometers through hell, sir,' said the sergeant. Mitty finished one last brandy. 'After all,' he said softly, 'what isn't?' The pounding of the cannon increased; there was the rat-tatting of machine guns, and from somewhere came the menacing pocketa-pocketa-pocketa of the new flame-throwers. Walter Mitty walked to the door of the dugout humming 'Auprès de Ma Blonde.' He turned and waved to the sergeant. 'Cheerio!' he said. . . .

Something struck his shoulder. 'I've been looking all over this hotel for you,' said Mrs Mitty. 'Why do you have to hide in this old chair? How did you expect me to find you?' 'Things close in,' said Walter Mitty vaguely. 'What?' Mrs Mitty said. 'Did you get the what's-its-name? The puppy biscuit? What's in that box?' 'Overshoes,' said Mitty. 'Couldn't you have put them on in the store?' 'I was thinking,' said Walter Mitty. 'Does it ever occur to you that I am sometimes thinking?' She looked at him. 'I'm going to take your temperature when I get you home,' she said.

They went out through the revolving doors that made a faintly derisive whistling sound when you pushed them. It was two blocks to the parking lot. At the drugstore on the corner she said, 'Wait here for me. I forgot something. I won't be a minute.' She was more than a minute. Walter Mitty lighted a cigarette. It began to rain, rain with sleet in it. He stood up against the wall of the drugstore, smoking. . . . He put his shoulders back and his heels together. 'To hell with the handkerchief,' said Walter Mitty scornfully. He took one last drag on his cigarette and snapped it away. Then, with that faint, fleeting smile playing about his lips, he faced the firing squad; erect and motionless, proud and disdainful, Walter Mitty the Undefeated, inscrutable to the last.

Interview with a Lemming

THE WEARY scientist, tramping through the mountains of northern Europe in the winter weather, dropped his knapsack and prepared to sit on a rock.

'Careful, brother,' said a voice.

'Sorry,' murmured the scientist, noting with some surprise that a lemming which he had been about to sit on had addressed him. 'It is a source of considerable astonishment to me,' said the scientist, sitting down beside the lemming, 'that you are capable of speech.'

'You human beings are always astonished,' said the lemming, 'when any other animal can do anything you can. Yet there are many things animals can do that you cannot, such as stridulate, or chirr, to name just one. To stridulate, or chirr, one of the minor achievements of the cricket, your species is dependent on the intestines of the sheep and the hair of the horse.'

'We are a dependent animal,' admitted the scientist.

'You are an amazing animal,' said the lemming.

'We have always considered you rather amazing, too,' said the scientist. 'You are perhaps the most mysterious of creatures.'

'If we are going to indulge in adjectives beginning with

"m,"' said the lemming, sharply, 'let me apply a few to your species – murderous, maladjusted, maleficent, malicious and muffle-headed.'

'You find our behavior as difficult to understand as we do yours?'

'You, as you would say, said it,' said the lemming. 'You kill, you mangle, you torture, you imprison, you starve each other. You cover the nurturing earth with cement, you cut down elm trees to put up institutions for people driven insane by the cutting down of elm trees, you—'

'You could go on all night like that,' said the scientist, 'listing our sins and our shames.'

'I could go on all night and up to four o'clock tomorrow afternoon,' said the lemming. 'It just happens that I have made a lifelong study of the self-styled higher animal. Except for one thing, I know all there is to know about you, and a singularly dreary, dolorous and distasteful store of information it is, too, to use only adjectives beginning with "d."'

'You say you have made a lifelong study of my species—' began the scientist.

'Indeed I have,' broke in the lemming. 'I know that you

are cruel, cunning and carnivorous, sly, sensual and selfish, greedy, gullible and guileful—'

'Pray don't wear yourself out,' said the scientist, quietly. 'It may interest you to know that I have made a lifelong study of lemmings, just as you have made a lifelong study of people. Like you, I have found but one thing about my subject which I do not understand.'

'And what is that?' asked the lemming.

'I don't understand,' said the scientist, 'why you lemmings all rush down to the sea and drown yourselves.'

'How curious,' said the lemming. 'The one thing I don't understand is why you human beings don't.'

You Could Look it Up

IT ALL begun when we dropped down to C'lumbus, Ohio, from Pittsburgh to play a exhibition game on our way out to St Louis. It was gettin' on into September, and though we'd been leadin' the league by six, seven games most of the season, we was now in first place by a margin you could 'a' got it into the eye of a thimble, bein' only a half a game ahead of St Louis. Our slump had given the boys the leapin' jumps, and they was like a bunch of old ladies at a lawn fete with a thunderstorm comin' up, runnin' around snarlin' at each other, eatin' bad and sleepin' worse, and battin' for a team average of maybe .186. Half the time nobody'd speak to nobody else, without it was to bawl 'em out.

Squawks Magrew was managin' the boys at the time, and he was darn near crazy. They called him 'Squawks' 'cause when things was goin' bad he lost his voice, or perty near lost it, and squealed at you like a little girl you stepped on her doll or somethin'. He yelled at everybody and wouldn't listen to nobody, without maybe it was me. I'd been trainin' the boys for ten year, and he'd take more lip from me than from anybody else. He knowed I was smarter'n him, anyways, like you're goin' to hear.

This was thirty, thirty-one year ago; you could look it up,

'cause it was the same year C'lumbus decided to call itself the Arch City, on account of a lot of iron arches with electric-light bulbs into 'em which stretched acrost High Street. Thomas Albert Edison sent 'em a telegram, and they was speechless and maybe even President Taft opened the celebrations by pushin' a button. It was a great week for the Buckeye capital, which was why they got us out there for this exhibition game.

Well, we just lose a double-header to Pittsburgh, 11 to 15 and 7 to 3, so we snarled all the way to C'lumbus, where we put up at the Chittaden Hotel, still snarlin'. Everybody was tetchy, and when Billy Klinger took a sock at Whitey Cott at breakfast, Whitey throwed marmalade all over his face.

'Blind each other, whatta I care?' says Magrew. 'You can't see nothin' anyways.'

C'lumbus win the exhibition game, 3 to 2, whilst Magrew set in the dugout, mutterin' and cursin' like a fourteen-year-old Scotty. He bad-mouthed everybody on the ball club and he bad-mouthed everybody offa the ball club, includin' the Wright brothers, who, he claimed, had yet to build an airship big enough for any of our boys to hit it with a ball bat.

'I wisht I was dead,' he says to me. 'I wisht I was in heaven with the angels.'

I told him to pull hisself together, 'cause he was drivin' the boys crazy, the way he was goin' on, sulkin' and bad-mouthin' and whinin'. I was older'n he was and smarter'n he was, and he knowed it. I was ten time smarter'n he was about this Pearl du Monville, first time I ever laid eyes on the little guy, which was one of the saddest days of my life.

Now, most people name of Pearl is girls, but this Pearl du Monville was a man, if you could call a fella a man who was only thirty-four, thirty-five inches high. Pearl du Monville was a midget. He was part French and part Hungarian, and maybe even part Bulgarian or somethin'. I can see him now, a sneer on his little pushed-in pan, swingin' a bamboo cane and smokin' a big cigar. He had a gray suit with a big black check into it, and he had a gray felt hat with one of them rainbow-colored hatbands onto it, like the young fellas wore in them days. He talked like he was talkin' into a tin can, but he didn't have no foreign accent. He might a been fifteen or he might a been a hundred, you couldn't tell. Pearl du Monville.

After the game with C'lumbus, Magrew headed straight for the Chittaden bar — the train for St Louis wasn't goin' for three, four hours — and there he set, drinkin' rye and talkin' to this bartender.

'How I pity me, brother,' Magrew was tellin' this bartender. 'How I pity me.' That was alwuz his favorite tune. So he was settin' there, tellin' this bartender how heartbreakin' it was to be manager of a bunch of blindfolded circus clowns, when up pops this Pearl du Monville outa nowheres.

It give Magrew the leapin' jumps. He thought at first maybe the D.T.'s had come back on him; he claimed he'd had 'em once, and little guys had popped up all around him, wearin' red, white and blue hats.

'Go on, now!' Magrew yells. 'Get away from me!'

But the midget clumb up on a chair acrost the table from Magrew and says, 'I seen that game today, Junior, and you ain't got no ball club. What you got there, Junior,' he says, 'is a side show.'

'Whatta ya mean, "Junior"?' says Magrew, touchin' the little guy to satisfy hisself he was real.

'Don't pay him no attention, mister,' says the bartender. 'Pearl calls everybody "Junior," 'cause it alwuz turns out he's a year older'n anybody else.'

'Yeah?' says Magrew. 'How old is he?'

'How old are you, Junior?' says the midget.

'Who, me? I'm fifty-three,' says Magrew.

'Well, I'm fifty-four,' says the midget.

Magrew grins and asts him what he'll have, and that was the beginnin' of their beautiful friendship, if you don't care what you say.

Pearl du Monville stood up on his chair and waved his cane around and pretended like he was ballyhooin' for a circus. 'Right this way, folks!' he yells. 'Come on in and see the greatest collection of freaks in the world! See the armless pitchers, see the eyeless batters, see the infielders with five thumbs!' and on and on like that, feedin' Magrew gall and handin' him a laugh at the same time, you might say.

You could hear him and Pearl du Monville hootin' and hollerin' and singin' way up to the fourth floor of the Chittaden, where the boys was packin' up. When it come time to go to the station, you can imagine how disgusted we was when we crowded into the doorway of that bar and seen them two singin' and goin' on.

'Well, well, well,' says Magrew, lookin' up and spottin' us. 'Look who's here. . . . Clowns, this is Pearl du Monville, a monseer of the old, old school. . . . Don't shake hands with 'em, Pearl, 'cause their fingers is made of chalk and would bust right off in your paws,' he says, and he starts guffawin' and Pearl starts titterin' and we stand there givin' 'em the iron eye, it bein' the lowest ebb a ball-club manager'd got hisself down to since the national pastime was started.

Then the midget begun givin' us the ballyhoo. 'Come on in!' he says, wavin' his cane. 'See the legless base runners, see the outfielders with the butter fingers, see the southpaw with the arm of a little chee-ild!'

Then him and Magrew begun to hoop and holler and nudge each other till you'd of thought this little guy was the funniest guy than even Charlie Chaplin. The fellas filed outa the bar without a word and went on up to the Union Depot, leavin' me to handle Magrew and his new-found crony.

Well, I got 'em outa there finely. I had to take the little guy along, 'cause Magrew had a holt onto him like a vise and I couldn't pry him loose.

'He's comin' along as masket,' says Magrew, holdin' the midget in the crouch of his arm like a football. And come along he did, hollerin' and protestin' and beatin' at Magrew with his little fists.

'Cut it out, will ya, Junior,' the little guy kept whinin'. 'Come on, leave a man loose, will ya, Junior?'

But Junior kept a holt onto him and begun yellin', 'See the guys with the glass arm, see the guys with the cast-iron brains, see the fielders with the feet on their wrists!'

So it goes, right through the whole Union Depot, with people starin' and catcallin', and he don't put the midget down till he gets him through the gates.

'How'm I goin' to go along without no toothbrush?' the midget asks. 'What'm I goin' to do without no other suit?' he says.

'Doc here,' says Magrew, meanin' me – 'doc here will look after you like you was his own son, won't you, doc?'

I give him the iron eye, and he finely got on the train and prob'ly went to sleep with his clothes on.

This left me alone with the midget. 'Lookit,' I says to him. 'Why don't you go on home now? Come mornin', Magrew'll forget all about you. He'll prob'ly think you was somethin' he seen in a nightmare maybe. And he ain't goin' to laugh so easy in the mornin', neither,' I says. 'So why don't you go on home?'

'Nix,' he says to me. 'Skidoo,' he says, 'twenty-three for you,' and he tosses his cane up into the vestibule of the coach and clam'ers on up after it like a cat. So that's the way Pearl du Monville come to go to St Louis with the ball club.

I seen 'em first at breakfast the next day, settin' opposite each other; the midget playin' 'Turkey in the Straw' on a harmonium and Magrew starin' at his eggs and bacon like they was a uncooked bird with its feathers still on.

'Remember where you found this?' I says, jerkin' my thumb at the midget. 'Or maybe you think they come with breakfast on these trains,' I says, bein' a good hand at turnin' a sharp remark in them days.

The midget puts down the harmonium and turns on me. 'Sneeze,' he says; 'your brains is dusty.' Then he snaps a couple of drops of water at me from a tumbler. 'Drown,' he says, tryin' to make his voice deep.

Now, both them cracks is Civil War cracks, but you'd of thought they was brand new and the funniest than any crack Magrew'd ever heard in his whole life. He started hoopin' and hollerin', and the midget started hoopin' and hollerin', so I walked on away and set down with Bugs Courtney and Hank Metters, payin' no attention to this weak-minded Damon and Phidias acrost the aisle.

Well, sir, the first game with St Louis was rained out, and there we was facin' a double-header next day. Like maybe I told you, we lose the last three double-headers we play, makin' maybe twenty-five errors in the six games, which is all right for the intimates of a school for the blind, but is disgraceful for the world's champions. It was too wet to go to the zoo, and Magrew wouldn't let us go to the movies, 'cause they flickered so bad in them days. So we just set around, stewin' and frettin'.

One of the newspaper boys come over to take a pitture of Billy Klinger and Whitey Cott shakin' hands – this reporter'd heard about the fight – and whilst they was standin' there, toe to toe, shakin' hands, Billy give a back lunge and a jerk, and throwed Whitey over his shoulder into the corner of the room, like a sack of salt. Whitey come back at him with a chair, and Bethlehem broke loose in that there room. The camera was tromped to pieces like a berry basket. When we finely got 'em pulled apart, I heard a laugh, and there was Magrew and the midget standin' in the door and givin' us the iron eye.

'Wrasslers,' says Magrew, cold-like, 'that's what I got for a ball club, Mr Du Monville, wrasslers – and not very good wrasslers at that, you ast me.'

'A man can't be good at everythin',' says Pearl, 'but he oughta be good at somethin'.'

This sets Magrew guffawin' again, and away they go, the midget taggin' along by his side like a hound dog and handin' him a fast line of so-called comic cracks.

When we went out to face that battlin' St Louis club in a double-header the next afternoon, the boys was jumpy as tin toys with keys in their back. We lose the first game, 7 to 2, and are trailin', 4 to 0, when the second game ain't but ten minutes old. Magrew set there like a stone statue, speakin' to nobody. Then, in the half a the fourth, somebody singled to center and knocked in two more runs for St Louis.

That made Magrew squawk. 'I wisht one thing,' he says. 'I wisht I was manager of a old ladies' sewin' circus 'stead of a ball club.'

'You are, Junior, you are,' says a familyer and disagreeable voice.

It was that Pearl du Monville again, poppin' up outa nowheres, swingin' his bamboo cane and smokin' a cigar that's three sizes too big for his face. By this time we'd finely got the other side out, and Hank Metters slithered a bat acrost the ground, and the midget had to jump to keep both his ankles from bein' broke.

I thought Magrew'd bust a blood vessel. 'You hurt Pearl and I'll break your neck!' he yelled.

Hank muttered somethin' and went on up to the plate and struck out.

We managed to get a couple of runs acrost in our half a the sixth, but they come back with three more in their half a the seventh, and this was too much for Magrew.

'Come on, Pearl,' he says. 'We're gettin' outa here.'

'Where do you think you're goin'?' I ast him.

'To the lawyer's again,' he says cryptly.

'I didn't know you'd been to the lawyer's once, yet,' I says.

'Which that goes to show how much you don't know,' he says.

With that, they was gone, and I didn't see 'em the rest of the day, nor know what they was up to, which was a God's blessin'. We lose the nightcap, 9 to 3, and that puts us into second place plenty, and as low in our mind as a ball club can get.

The next day was a horrible day, like anybody that lived through it can tell you. Practice was just over and the St Louis club was takin' the field, when I hears this strange sound from the stands. It sounds like the nervous whickerin' a horse gives when he smell somethin' funny on the wind. It was the fans ketchin' sight of Pearl du Monville, like you have prob'ly guessed. The midget had popped up onto the field all dressed up in a minacher club uniform, sox, cap, little letters sewed onto his chest, and all. He was swingin' a kid's bat and the only thing kept him from lookin' like a real ballplayer seen through the wrong end of a microscope was this cigar he was smokin'.

Bugs Courtney reached over and jerked it outa his mouth and throwed it away. 'You're wearin' that suit on the playin' field,' he says to him, severe as a judge. 'You go insultin' it and I'll take you out to the zoo and feed you to the bears.'

Pearl just blowed some smoke at him which he still has in his mouth.

Whilst Whitey was foulin' off four or five prior to strikin' out, I went on over to Magrew. 'If I was as comic as you,' I says, 'I'd laugh myself to death,' I says. 'Is that any way to treat the uniform, makin' a mockery out of it?'

'It might surprise you to know I ain't makin' no mockery outa the uniform,' says Magrew. 'Pearl du Monville here has been made a bone-of-fida member of this so-called ball club. I fixed it up with the front office by long-distance phone.'

'Yeh?' I says. 'I can just hear Mr Dillworth or Bart Jenkins agreein' to hire a midget for the ball club. I can just hear 'em.' Mr Dillworth was the owner of the club and Bart Jenkins was the secretary, and they never stood for no monkey business. 'May I be so bold as to inquire,' I says, 'just what you told 'em?'

'I told 'em,' he says, 'I wanted to sign up a guy they ain't no pitcher in the league can strike him out.'

'Uh-huh,' I says, 'and did you tell 'em what size of a man he is?'

'Never mind about that,' he says. 'I got papers on me, made out legal and proper, constitutin' one Pearl du Monville a bone-of-fida member of this former ball club. Maybe that'll shame them big babies into gettin' in there and swingin', knowin' I can replace any one of 'em with a midget, if I have a mind to. A St Louis lawyer I seen twice tells me it's all legal and proper.'

'A St Louis lawyer would,' I says, 'seein' nothin' could make him happier than havin' you makin' a mockery outa this one-time baseball outfit,' I says.

Well, sir, it'll all be there in the papers of thirty, thirty-one years ago, and you could look it up. The game went along without no scorin' for seven innings, and since they ain't nothin' much to watch but guys poppin' up or strikin' out, the fans pay most of their attention to the goin's-on of Pearl du Monville. He's out there in front a the dugout, turnin' handsprings, balancin' his bat on his chin, walkin' a imaginary line, and so on. The fans clapped and laughed at him, and he ate it up.

So it went up to the last a the eighth, nothin' to nothin'; not more'n seven, eight hits all told, and no errors on neither side. Our pitcher gets the first two men out easy in the eighth. Then up come a fella name of Porter or Billings, or some such name, and he lammed one up against the tobacco sign for three bases. The next guy up slapped the first ball out into left for a base hit, and in come the fella from third for the only run of the ball game so far. The crowd yelled, the look a death come onto Magrew's face again, and even the midget quit his tom-foolin'. They next man fouled out back a third, and we come up for our last bats like a bunch a schoolgirls steppin' into a pool of cold water. I was lower in my mind than I'd been since the day in Nineteen-four when Chesbro throwed the wild pitch in the ninth inning with a man on third and lost the pennant for the Highlanders. I knowed something just as bad was goin' to happen, which shows I'm a clairvoyun, or was then.

When Gordy Mills hit out to second, I just closed my eyes. I opened 'em up again to see Dutch Muller standin' on second, dustin' off his pants, him havin' got his first hit in maybe twenty times to the plate. Next up was Harry Loesing, battin' for our pitcher, and he got a base on balls, walkin' on a fourth one you could a combed your hair with.

Then up come Whitey Cott, our lead-off man. He crotches

down in what was prob'ly the most fearsome stanch in organized ball, but all he can do is pop out to short. That brung up Billy Klinger, with two down and a man on first and second. Billy took a cut at one you could a knocked a plug hat offa this here Carnera with it, but then he gets sense enough to wait 'em out, and finely he walks, too, fillin' the bases.

Yes, sir, there you are; the tyin' run on third and the winnin' run on second, first a the ninth, two men down, and Hank Metters comin' to the bat. Hank was built like a Pope-Hartford and he couldn't run no faster'n President Taft, but he had five home runs to his credit for the season, and that wasn't bad in them days. Hank was still hittin' better'n anybody else on the ball club, and it was mighty heartenin', seein' him stridin' up towards the plate. But he never got there.

'Wait a minute!' yells Magrew, jumpin' to his feet. 'I'm sendin' in a pinch hitter!' he yells.

You could have heard a bomb drop. When a ball-club manager says he sendin' in a pinch hitter for the best batter on the club, you know and I know and everybody knows he's lost his holt.

'They're goin' to be sendin' the funny wagon for you, if you don't watch out,' I says, grabbin' a holt of his arm.

But he pulled away and run out towards the plate, yellin', 'Du Monville, battin' for Metters!'

All the fellas begun squawlin' at once, except Hank, and he just stood there starin' at Magrew like he'd gone crazy and was claimin' to be Ty Cobb's grandma or somethin'. Their pitcher stood out there with his hands on his hips and a disagreeable look on his face, and the plate umpire told Magrew to go on and get a batter up. Magrew told him again Du Monville was battin' for Metters, and the St Louis manager finely got the idea. It brung him outa his dugout, howlin' and bawlin' like he'd lost a female dog and her seven pups.

Magrew pushed the midget towards the plate and he says to him, he says, 'Just stand up there and hold that bat on your shoulder. They ain't a man in the world can throw three strikes in there 'fore he throws four balls!' he says.

'I get it, Junior!' says the midget. 'He'll walk me and force in the tyin' run!' And he starts on up to the plate as cocky as if he was Willie Keeler.

I don't need to tell you Bethlehem broke loose on that there ball field. The fans got on to their hind legs, yellin' and whistlin', and everybody on the field begun wavin' their arms and hollerin' and shovin'. The plate umpire stalked over to Magrew like a traffic cop, waggin' his jaw and pointin' his finger, and the St Louis manager kept yellin' like his house was on fire. When Pearl got up to the plate and stood there, the pitcher slammed his glove down onto the ground and started stompin' on it, and they ain't nobody can blame him. He's just walked two normal-sized human bein's, and now here's a guy up to the plate they ain't more'n twenty inches between his knees and his shoulders.

The plate umpire called in the field umpire, and they talked a while, like a couple of doctors seein' the bucolic plague, or somethin' for the first time. Then the plate umpire come over to Magrew with his arms folded acrost his chest, and he told him to go on and get a batter up, or he'd forfeit the game to St Louis. He pulled out his watch, but somebody batted it outa his hand in the scufflin', and I thought there'd be a free-for-all, with everybody yellin' and shovin' except Pearl du Monville, who stood up at the plate with his little bat on his shoulder, not movin' a muscle.

Then Magrew played his ace. I seen him pull some papers outa his pocket and show 'em to the plate umpire. The umpire begun lookin' at 'em like they was bills for somethin' he not only never bought it, he never even heard of it. The other umpire studied 'em like they was a death warren, and all this time the St Louis manager and the fans and the players is yellin' and hollerin'.

Well, sir, they fought about him bein' a midget, and they fought about him usin' a kid's bat, and they fought about where'd he been all season. They was eight or nine rule books brung out and everybody was thumbin' through 'em, tryin' to find out what it says about midgets, but it don't say nothin' about midgets, 'cause this was somethin' never'd come up in the history of the game before, and nobody'd ever dreamed about it, even when they has nightmares. Maybe you can't send no midgets in to bat nowadays, 'cause the old game's changed a lot, mostly for the worst, but you could then, it turned out.

The plate umpire finely decided the contrack papers were all legal and proper, like Magrew said, so he waved the St. Louis players back to their places and he pointed his finger at their manager and told him to quit hollerin' and get on back in the dugout. The manager says the game is percedin' under protest, and the umpire bawls, 'Play ball!' over 'n' above the yellin' and booin', him havin' a voice like a hog-caller.

The St Louis pitcher picked up his glove and beat at it with his fist six or eight times, and then got set on the mound and studied the situation. The fans realized he was really goin' to pitch to the midget, and they went crazy, hoopin' and hollerin' louder'n ever, and throwin' pop bottles and hats and cushions down onto the field. It took five, ten minutes to get the fans quieted down again, whilst our fellas that was on base set down on the bags and waited. And Pearl du Monville kept standin' up there with the bat on his shoulder, like he'd been told to.

So the pitcher starts studyin' the setup again, and you got to admit it was the strangest setup in a ball game since the players cut off their beards and begun wearin' gloves. I wisht I could call the pitcher's name – it wasn't old Barney Pelty nor Nig Jack Powell nor Harry Howell. He was a big right-hander, but I can't call his name. You could look it up. Even in a crotchin' position, the ketcher towers over the midget like the Washington Monument.

The plate umpire tries standin' on his tiptoes, then he tries crotchin' down, and he finely gets hisself into a stanch nobody'd ever seen on a ball field before, kinda squattin' down on his haunches.

Well, the pitcher is sore as a old buggy horse in fly time. He slams in the first pitch, hard and wild, and maybe two foot higher'n the midget's head.

'Ball one!' hollers the umpire over 'n' above the racket, 'cause everybody is yellin' worsten ever.

The ketcher goes on out towards the mound and talks to

the pitcher and hands him the ball. This time the big right-hander tried a undershoot, and it comes in a little closer, maybe no higher'n a foot, foot and a half above Pearl's head. It would a been a strike with a human bein' in there, but the umpire's got to call it, and he does.

'Ball two!' he bellers.

The ketcher walks on out to the mound again, and the whole infield comes over and gives advice to the pitcher about what they'd do in a case like this, with two balls and no strikes on a batter that oughta be in a bottle of alcohol 'stead of up there at the plate in a big-league game between the teams that is fightin' for first place.

For the third pitch, the pitcher stands there flat-footed and tosses up the ball like he's playin' ketch with a little girl.

Pearl stands there motionless as a hitchin' post, and the ball comes in big and slow and high – high for Pearl, that is, it bein' about on a level with his eyes, or a little higher'n a grown man's knees.

They ain't nothin' else for the umpire to do, so he calls, 'Ball three!'

Everybody is onto their feet, hoopin' and hollerin', as the pitcher sets to throw ball four. The St Louis manager is makin' signs and faces like he was a contorturer, and the infield is givin' the pitcher some more advice about what to do this time. Our boys who was on base stick right onto the bag, runnin' no risk of bein' nipped for the last out.

Well, the pitcher decides to give him a toss again, seein' he come closer with that than with a fast ball. They ain't nobody ever seen a slower ball throwed. It come in big as a balloon and slower'n any ball ever throwed before in the major leagues. It come right in over the plate in front of Pearl's chest, lookin' prob'ly big as a full moon to Pearl. They ain't never been a minute like the minute that followed since the United States was founded by the Pilgrim grandfathers.

Pearl du Monville took a cut at that ball, and he hit it! Magrew give a groan like a poleaxed steer as the ball rolls out in front a the plate into fair territory.

'Fair ball!' yells the umpire, and the midget starts runnin' for first, still carryin' that little bat, and makin' maybe ninety foot an hour. Bethlehem breaks loose on that ball field and in them stands. They ain't never been nothin' like it since creation was begun.

The ball's rollin' slow, on down towards third, goin' maybe eight, ten foot. The infield comes in fast and our boys break from their bases like hares in a brush fire. Everybody is standin' up, yellin' and hollerin', and Magrew is tearin' his hair outa his head, and the midget is scamperin' for first with all the speed of one of them little dashhounds carryin' a satchel in his mouth.

The ketcher gets to the ball first, but he boots it on out past the pitcher's box, the pitcher fallin' on his face tryin' to stop it, the shortstop sprawlin' after it full length and zaggin' it on over towards the second baseman, whilst Muller is scorin' with the tyin' run and Loesing is roundin' third with the winnin' run. Ty Cobb could a made a three-bagger outa that bunt, with everybody fallin' over theirself trying to pick the ball up. But Pearl is still maybe fifteen, twenty feet from the bag, toddlin' like a baby and yeepin' like a trapped rabbit, when the second baseman finely gets a holt of that ball and slams it over to first. The first baseman ketches it and stomps on the bag, the base umpire waves Pearl out, and there goes your old ball game, the craziest ball game ever played in the history of the organized world.

Their players start runnin' in, and then I see Magrew. He starts after Pearl, runnin' faster'n any man ever run before. Pearl sees him comin' and runs behind the base umpire's legs and gets a holt onto 'em. Magrew comes up, pantin' and roarin', and him and the midget plays ring-around-a-rosy with the umpire, who keeps shovin' at Magrew with one hand and tryin' to slap the midget loose from his legs with the other.

Finely Magrew ketches the midget, who is still yeepin' like a stuck sheep. He gets holt of that little guy by both his ankles and starts whirlin' him round and round his head like Magrew was a hammer thrower and Pearl was the hammer. Nobody can stop him without gettin' their head knocked off, so everybody just stands there and yells. Then Magrew lets the midget fly. He flies on out towards, second, high and fast, like a human home run, headed for the soap sign in center field.

Their shortstop tries to get to him, but he can't make it, and I knowed the little fella was goin' to bust to pieces like a dollar watch on a asphalt street when he hit the ground. But it so happens their center fielder is just crossin' second, and he starts runnin' back, tryin' to get under the midget, who had took to spiralin' like a football 'stead of turnin' head over foot, which give him more speed and more distance.

I know you never seen a midget ketched, and you prob'ly never even seen one throwed. To ketch a midget that's been thrown by a heavy-muscled man and is flyin' through the air, you got to run under him and with him and pull your hands and arms back and down when you ketch him, to break the compact of his body, or you'll bust him in two like a matchstick. I seen Bill Lange and Willie Keeler and Tris Speaker make some wonderful ketches in my day, but I never seen nothin' like that center fielder. He goes back and back and still further back and he pulls that midget down outa the air like he was liftin' a sleepin' baby from a cradle. They wasn't a bruise on to him, only his face was the color of cat's meat and he ain't got no air in his chest. In his excitement, the base umpire, who was runnin' back with the center fielder when he ketched Pearl, yells, 'Out!' and that give hysteries to the Bethlehem which was ragin' like Niagry on that ball field.

Everybody was hoopin' and hollerin' and yellin' and runnin', with the fans swarmin' onto the field, and the cops tryin' to keep order, and some guys laughin' and some of the women fans cryin', and six or eight of us holdin' onto Magrew to keep him from gettin' at that midget and finishin' him off. Some of the fans picks up the St Louis pitcher and the center fielder, and starts carryin' 'em around on their shoulders, and they was the craziest goin's-on knowed to the history of organized ball on this side of the 'Lantic Ocean.

I seen Pearl du Monville strugglin' in the arms of a lady fan with a ample bosom, who was laughin' and cryin' at the same time, and him beatin' at her with his little fists and bawlin' and yellin'. He clawed his way loose finely and disappeared in the forest of legs which made that ball field look like it was Coney Island on a hot summer's day.

That was the last I ever seen of Pearl du Monville. I never seen hide nor hair of him from that day to this, and neither did anybody else. He just vanished into the thin of the air, as the fella says. He was ketched for the final out of the ball game and that was the end of him, just like it was the end of the ball game, you might say, and also the end of our losin' streak, like I'm goin' to tell you.

That night we piled onto a train for Chicago, but we wasn't snarlin' and snappin' any more. No, sir, the ice was finely broke and a new spirit come into that ball club. The old zip come back with the disappearance of Pearl du Monville out back a second base. We got to laughin' and talkin' and kiddin' together, and 'fore long Magrew was laughin' with us. He got a human look onto his pan again, and he quit whinin' and complainin' and wishtin' he was in heaven with the angels.

Well, sir, we wiped up that Chicago series, winnin' all four games, and makin' seventeen hits in one of 'em. Funny thing was, St Louis was so shook up by that last game with us, they never did hit their stride again. Their center fielder took to misjudgin' everything that come his way, and the rest a the fellas followed suit, the way a club'll do when one guy blows up.

'Fore we left Chicago, I and some of the fellas went out and bought a pair of them little baby shoes, which we had 'em golded over and give 'em to Magrew for a souvenir, and he took it all in good spirit. Whitey Cott and Billy Klinger made up and was fast friends again, and we hit our home lot like a ton of dynamite and they was nothin' could stop us from then on.

I don't recollect things as clear as I did thirty, forty year ago. I can't read no fine print no more, and the only person I got to check with on the golden days of the national pastime, as the fella says, is my friend, old Milt Kline, over in Springfield, and his mind ain't as strong as it once was.

He gets Rube Waddell mixed up with Rube Marquard, for one thing, and anybody does that oughta be put away where he won't bother nobody. So I can't tell you the exact margin we win the pennant by. Maybe it was two and a half games, or maybe it was three and a half. But it'll all be there in the newspapers and record books of thirty, thirty-one year ago and, like I was sayin', you could look it up.

A Ride With Olympy

OLYMPY SEMENTZOFF called me '*Monsieur*' because I was the master of the Villa Tamisier and he was the gardener, the Russian husband of the French caretaker, Maria. I called him '*Monsieur*,' too, because I could never learn to call any man Olympy and because there was a wistful air of *ancien régime* about him. He drank Bénédictine with me and smoked my cigarettes; he also, as you will see, drove my car. We conversed in French, a language alien to both of us, but more alien to me than to him. He said '*gauche*' for both 'right' and 'left' when he was upset, but when I was upset I was capable of flights that put the French people on their guard, wide-eyed and wary. Once, for instance, when I cut my wrist on a piece of glass I ran into the lobby of a hotel shouting in French, 'I am sick with a knife!' Olympy would have known what to say (except that it would have been his left wrist in any case) but he wouldn't have shouted: his words ran softly together and sounded something like the burbling of water over stones. Often I did not know what he was talking about; rarely did he know what I was talking about. There was a misty, faraway quality about this relationship, in French, of Russia and Ohio. The fact that the accident Olympy and I were involved in fell short of a catastrophe was, in view of everything, something of a miracle.

Olympy and Maria 'came with' the villa my wife and I rented on Cap d'Antibes. Maria was a deep-bosomed, large-waisted woman, as persistently pleasant as Riviera weather in a good season; no mistral ever blew in the even climate of her temperament. She must have been more than forty-five but she was as strong as a root; once when I had trouble getting a tough cork out of a wine bottle she took hold and whisked it out as if it had been a maidenhair fern. On Sundays her son came over from the barracks in Antibes and we all had a glass of white Bordeaux together, sometimes the Sementzoffs' wine, sometimes our own. Her son was eighteen and a member of the Sixth Regiment of Chasseurs Alpins, a tall, somber boy, handsome in his uniform and cape. He was an *enfant du premier lit*, as the French say. Maria made her first bed with a sergeant of the army who was *cordonnier* for his regiment during the war and seemed somehow to have laid by quite a little money. After the war the sergeant-shoemaker resigned from the army, put his money in investments of some profoundly mysterious nature in Indo-China, and lost it all. '*Il est mort*,' Maria told us, '*de chagrin*.' Grief over his ill-fortune brought on a decline; the *chagrin*, Maria said, finally reached his brain, and he died at the age of thirty-eight. Maria had to sell their house to pay the taxes, and go to work.

Olympy Sementzoff, Maria's second husband, was shy, not very tall, and wore a beard; in his working clothes you didn't notice much more than that. When he was dressed for Sunday – he wore a fine double-breasted jacket – you observed that his mouth was sensitive, his eyes attractively sad, and that he wore his shyness with a certain air. He worked in a boat factory over near Cannes – Maria said that he was a *spécialiste de bateaux*; odd jobs about the villa grounds he did on his off days. It was scarcely light when he got up in the morning, for he had to be at work at seven; it was almost dark when he got home. He was paid an incredibly small amount for what he did at the factory and a handful of sous each month for what he did about the grounds. When I gave him a hundred francs for some work he had done for me in the house – he could repair anything from a drain to a watch – he said, '*Oh, monsieur, c'est trop!*' '*Mais non, monsieur,*' said I. '*Ce n'est pas beaucoup.*' He took it finally, after an exchange of bows and compliments.

The elderly wife of the Frenchman from whom we rented the villa told us, in a dark whisper, that Olympy was a White Russian and that there was perhaps a *petit mystère* about him, but we figured this as her own fanciful bourgeois alarm. Maria did not make a mystery out of her husband. There was the Revolution, most of Olympy's brothers and sisters were killed – one knew how that was – and he escaped. He was, of course, an exile and must not go back. If she knew just who he was in Russia and what he had done, she didn't make it very clear. He was in Russia and he escaped; she had married him thirteen years before; *et puis, voilà!* It would have been nice to believe that there was the blood of the Czars in Olympy, but if there was anything to the ancient legend that all the stray members of the Imperial House took easily and naturally to driving a taxi, that let Olympy out. He was not a born chauffeur, as I found out the day I came back from our automobile ride on foot and – unhappily for Maria – alone.

Olympy Sementzoff rode to and from his work in one of those bastard agglomerations of wheels, motor and super-structure that one saw only in France. It looked at first glance like the cockpit of a cracked-up plane. Then you saw that there were two wheels in front and a single wheel in back. Except for the engine – which Maria said was a 'Morgan *moteur*' – and the wheels and tires, it was hand-made. Olympy's boss at the boat factory had made most of it, but Olympy himself had put on the *ailes*, or fenders, which were made of some kind of wood. The strange canopy that served as a top was Maria's proud handiwork; it seemed to have been made of canvas and kitchen aprons. The thing had a right-hand drive. When the *conducteur* was in his seat he was very low to the ground: you had to bend down to talk to him. There was a small space beside the driver in which another person could sit, or crouch. The whole affair was not much larger than an overturned cabinet victrola. It got bouncingly under way with all the racket of a dog fight and in full swing was capable of perhaps thirty miles an hour. The contraption had cost Olympy three thousand francs, or about a hundred dollars. He had driven it for three years and was hand in glove with its mysterious mechanism. The gadgets on the dash and on the floorboard, which he pulled or pushed to make the thing go, seemed to include fire tongs, spoons, and door-knobs. Maria miraculously managed to squeeze into the seat beside the driver in an emergency, but I could understand why she didn't want to drive to the Nice Carnival in the 'Morgan.' It was because she didn't that I suggested Olympy should take her over one day in my Ford sedan. Maria had given us to understand that her *mari* could drive any car – he could be a chauffeur if he wanted to, a *bon* chauffeur. All I would have to do, *voyez-vous*, was to take Olympy for a turn around the Cap so that he could get the hang of the big car. Thus is was that one day after lunch we set off.

Half a mile out of Antibes on the shore road, I stopped the car and changed places with Olympy, letting the engine run. Leaning forward, he took a tense grip on a steering wheel much larger than he was used to and too far away from him. I could see that he was nervous. He put his foot down on the clutch, tentatively, and said, *'Embrayage?'* He had me there. My knowledge of French automotive terms is inadequate and volatile. I was forced to say I didn't know. I couldn't remember the word for clutch in any of the three languages, French, Italian and German, in which it was given in my 'Motorist's Guide' (which was back at the villa). Somehow *'embrayage'* didn't sound right for clutch (it is, though). I knew it wouldn't do any good for an American writer to explain in French to a Russian boat specialist the purpose that particular pedal served; furthermore, I didn't really know. I compromised by putting my left foot on the brake. *'Frein,'* I said. *'Ah,'* said Olympy, unhappily. This method of indicating what something might be by demonstrating what it wasn't had a disturbing effect. I shifted my foot to the accelerator – or rather pointed my toe at it – and suddenly the word for that, even the French for gasoline, left me. I was growing a little nervous myself. *'Benzina,'* I said, in Italian finally. *'Ah?'* said Olympy. Whereas we had been one remove from reality to begin with, we were now two, or perhaps three, removes. A polyglot approach to the fine precision of a gas engine is roundabout and dangerous. We both lost a little confidence in each other. I suppose we should have given up right then, but we didn't.

Olympy decided the extra pedal was the *embrayage*, shifted into low from neutral, and the next thing I knew we were making a series of short forward bounds like a rabbit leaping out of a wheat field to see where he is. This form of locomotion takes a lot out of man and car. The engine complained in loud, rhythmic whines. And then Olympy somehow got his left foot on the starter and there was a familiar undertone of protest; this set his right foot to palpitating on the accelerator and the rabbit-jumps increased in scope. Abandoning my search for the word for starter, I grabbed his left knee and shouted *'Ça commence!'* Just what was commencing Olympy naturally couldn't figure – probably some habitual and ominous idiosyncrasy of the machinery. He gave me a quick, pale look. I shut off the ignition, and we discussed the starter situation, breathing a little heavily. He understood what it was finally, and presently we were lurching ahead again, Olympy holding her in low gear, like a wrestler in a clinch, afraid to risk shifting into second. He tried it at last and with a jamming jolt and a roar we went into reverse: the car writhed like a tortured leopard and the engine quit.

I was puzzled and scared, and so was Olympy. Only a

foolish pride in masculine fortitude kept us going. I showed him the little jog to the right you have to make to shift into second and he started the engine and we were off again, jolting and lurching. He made the shift, finally, with a noise like lightning striking a foundry – and veered swoopingly to the right. We barely missed a series of staunch granite blocks, set in concrete, that mark ditches and soft shoulders. We whisked past a pole. The leaves of a vine hanging on a wall slapped at me through the window. My voice left me. I was fascinated and paralyzed by the swift passes disaster was making at my head. At length I was able to grope blindly toward the ignition switch, but got my wrist on the klaxon button. When I jerked my arm away, Olympy began obediently sounding the horn. We were riding on the edge of a ditch. I managed somehow to shut off the ignition and we rolled to a stop. Olympy, unused to a left-hand drive, had forgotten there was a large portion of the car to his right, with me in it. I told him, '*A gauche, à gauche, toujours à gauche!*' '*Ah,*' said Olympy, but there was no comprehension in him. I could see he didn't know we had been up against the vines of villa walls: intent on the dark problem of gearshifting, he had been oblivious to where the car and I had been. There was a glint in his eye now. He was determined to get the thing into high on his next attempt; we had come about half a mile in the lower gears.

The road curved downhill as it passed Eden Roc and it was here that an elderly English couple, unaware of the fact that hell was loose on the highway, were walking. Olympy was in second again, leaning forward like a racing bicycle rider. I shouted at him to look out, he said '*Oui*' – and we grazed the old man and his wife. I glanced back in horror: they were staring at us, mouths and eyes wide, unable to move or make a sound. Olympy raced onto a new peril: a descending hairpin curve, which he negotiated in some far-fetched manner, with me hanging onto the emergency brake. The road straightened out, I let go the brake, and Olympy slammed into high with the desperate gesture of a man trying to clap his hat over a poised butterfly. We began to whiz: Olympy hadn't counted on a fast pickup. He whirled around a car in front of us with a foot to spare. '*Lentement!*' I shouted, and then '*Gauche!*' as I began to get again the whimper of poles and walls in my ears. '*Ça va mieux, maintenant*,' said Olympy, quietly. A wild thought ran through my head that maybe this was the way they used to drive in Russia in the old days.

Ahead of us now was one of the most treacherous curves on the Cap. The road narrowed and bent, like a croquet wicket, around a high stone wall that shut off your view of what was coming. What was coming was usually on the wrong side of the road, so it wouldn't do to shout '*Gauche!*' now. We made the turn all right. There was a car coming, but it was well over on its own side. Olympy apparently didn't think so. He whirled the wheel to the right, didn't take up the play fast enough in whirling it back, and there was a tremendous banging crash, like a bronze monument falling. I had a glimpse of Olympy's right hand waving around like the hand of a man hunting for something under a table. I didn't know what his feet were doing. We were still moving, heavily, with a ripping noise and a loud roar.

'*Poussez le phare!*' I shouted, which means 'push the headlight!' '*Ah-h-h-h,*' said Olympy. I shut off the ignition and pulled on the hand brake, but we had already stopped. We got out and looked at the pole we had sideswiped and at the car. The right front fender was crumpled and torn and the right back one banged up, but nothing else had been hurt. Olympy's face was so stricken when he looked at me that I felt I had to cheer him up. '*Il fait beau,*' I announced, which is to say that the weather is fine. It was all I could think of.

I started for a garage that Olympy knew about. At the first street we came he said '*Gauche*' and I turned left. '*Ah, non,*' said Olympy. '*Gauche,*' and he pointed the other way. 'You mean *droit?*' I asked, just that way. '*Ah!*' said Olympy. '*C'est bien ça!*' It was as if he had thought of something he hadn't been able to remember for days. That explained a great deal.

I left Olympy and the car at the garage; he said he would walk back. One of the garage men drove me into Juan-les-Pins and I walked home from there – and into a look of wild dismay in Maria's eyes. I hadn't thought about that: she had seen us drive away together and here I was, alone. '*Où est votre mari?*' I asked her, hurriedly. It was something of a failure as a reassuring beginning. I had taken the question out of her own mouth, so I answered it. 'He has gone for a walk,' I told her. Then I tried to say that her husband was *bon*, but I pronounced it *beau*, so that what I actually said was that her husband was handsome. She must have figured that he was not only dead but laid out. There was a *mauvais quart d'heure* for both of us before the drooping figure of Olympy finally appeared. He explained sadly to Maria that the mechanism of the Ford is strange and curious compared to the mechanism of the Morgan. I agreed with him. Of course, he protested, he would pay for the repairs to the car, but Maria and I both put down that suggestion. Maria's idea of my work was that I was paid by the City of New York and enjoyed a tremendous allowance. Olympy got forty francs a day at the boat factory.

That night, at dinner, Maria told me that her *mari* was pacing up and down in their little bedroom at the rear of the house. He was in a state. I didn't want an attack of *chagrin* to come on him as it had on the *cordonnier* and perhaps reach his brain. When Maria was ready to go we gave her a handful of cigarettes for Olympy and a glass of Bénédictine. The next day, at dawn, I hear the familiar *tintamarre* and *hurlement* and *brouhaha* of Olympy's wonderful contraption getting under way once more. He was off to the boat factory and his forty francs a day, his dollar and thirty cents. It would have cost him two weeks' salary to pay for the fenders, but he would have managed it somehow. When I went down to breakfast, Maria came in from the kitchen with a large volume, well fingered and full of loose pages, which she handed to me. It was called *Le Musée d'Art* and subtitled *Galerie des Chefs-d'oeuvre et Précis de l'Histoire de l'Art au XIXe Siècle, en France et à l'Etranger (1000 gravures, 58 planches hors texte)*. A present to *Monsieur* from Olympy Sementzoff, with his compliments. The incident of the automobile was thus properly rounded off with an exchange of presents: cigarettes,

Bénédictine, and *Le Musée d'Art*. It seemed to me the way such things should always end, but perhaps Olympy and I were ahead of our day – or behind it.

There's No Place Like Home

IDLING THROUGH a London bookstore in the summer of 1937, I came upon a little book called 'Collins' Pocket Interpreters: France.' Written especially to instruct the English how to speak French in the train, the hotel, the quandary, the dilemma, etc., it is, of course, equally useful – I might also say equally depressing – to Americans. I have come across a number of these helps-for-travelers, but none that has the heavy impact, the dark, cumulative power of Collins'. A writer in a London magazine mentions a phrase book got out in the era of Imperial Russia which contained this one magnificent line: 'Oh, dear, our postillion has been struck by lightning!' but that fantastic piece of disaster, while charming and provocative – though, I daresay, quite rare even in the days of the Czars – is to Mr Collins' modern, workaday disasters as Fragonard is to George Bellows, or Sarah Orne Jewett to William Faulkner. Let us turn the pages of this appalling little volume.

Each page has a list of English expressions one under the other, which gives them the form of verse. The French translations are run alongside. Thus, on the first page, under 'The Port of Arrival,' we begin (quietly enough) with 'Porter, here is my baggage!' – '*Porteur, voici mes bagages!*'

From then on disaster follows fast and follows faster until in the end, as you shall see, all hell breaks loose. The volume contains three times as many expressions to use when one is in trouble as when everything is going all right. This, my own experience has shown, is about the right ratio, but God spare me some of the difficulties for which the traveler is prepared in Mr Collins' melancholy narrative poem. I am going to leave out the French translations because, for one thing, people who get involved in the messes and tangles we are coming to invariably forget their French and scream in English anyway. Furthermore, the French would interrupt the fine, free flow of the English and spoil what amounts to a dramatic tragedy of an overwhelming and original kind. The phrases, as I have said, run one under the other, but herein I shall have to run them one after another (you can copy them down the other way, if you want to).

Trouble really starts in the canto called 'In the Customs Shed.' Here were have: 'I cannot open my case.' 'I have lost the keys.' 'Help me to close this case.' 'I did not know that I had to pay.' 'I don't want to pay so much.' 'I cannot find my porter.' 'Have you seen porter 153?' That last query is a little master stroke of writing, I think, for in those few words we have a graphic picture of a tourist lost in a jumble of thousands of bags and scores of customs men, looking frantically for one of at least a hundred and fifty-three porters. We feel that the tourist will not find porter 153, and the note of frustration has been struck.

Our tourist (accompanied by his wife, I like to think) finally gets on the train for Paris – having lost his keys and not having found his porter – and it comes time presently to go to the dining car, although he probably has no appetite, for the customs men, of course, have had to break open that one suitcase. Now, I think, it is the wife who begins to crumble: 'Someone has taken my seat.' 'Excuse me, sir, that seat is mine.' 'I cannot find my ticket!' 'I have left my ticket in the compartment.' 'I will go and look for it.' 'I have left my gloves (my purse) in the dining car.' Here the note of frenzied disintegration, so familiar to all travelers abroad, is sounded. Next comes 'The Sleeper,' which begins, ominously, with 'What is the matter?' and ends with 'May I open the window?' 'Can you open this window, please?' We realize, of course, that *nobody* is going to be able to open the window and that the tourist and his wife will suffocate. In this condition they arrive in Paris, and the scene there, on the crowded station platform, is done with superb economy of line: 'I have left something in the train.' 'A parcel, an overcoat.' 'A mackintosh, a stick.' 'An umbrella, a camera.' 'A fur, a suitcase.' The travelers have now begun to go completely to pieces, in the grand manner.

Next comes an effective little interlude about an airplane trip, which is one of my favorite passages in this swift and sorrowful tragedy: 'I want to reserve a place in the plane leaving tomorrow morning.' 'When do we start?' 'Can we get anything to eat on board?' 'When so we arrive?' 'I feel sick.' 'Have you any paper bags for air-sickness?' 'The noise is terrible.' 'Have you any cotton wool?' 'When are we going to land?' This brief masterpiece caused me to cancel an air trip from London to Paris and go the easy way, across the Channel.

We now come to a section called 'At the Hotel,' in which

THERE'S NO PLACE LIKE HOME

things go from worse to awful. 'Did you not get my letter?' 'I wrote to you three weeks ago.' 'I asked for a first-floor room.' 'If you can't give me something better, I shall go away.' 'The chambermaid never comes when I ring.' 'I cannot sleep at night, there is so much noise.' 'I have just had a wire. I must leave at once.' Panic has begun to set in, and it is not appeased any by the advent of 'The Chambermaid': 'Are you the chambermaid?' 'There are no towels here.' 'The sheets on this bed are damp.' 'This room is not clean.' 'I have seen a mouse in the room.' 'You will have to set a mouse trap here.' The bells of hell at this point begin to ring in earnest: 'These shoes are not mine.' 'I put my shoes here, where are they now?' 'The light is not good.' 'The bulb is broken.' 'The radiator is too warm.' 'The radiator doesn't work.' 'It is cold in this room.' 'This is not clean, bring me another.' 'I don't like this.' 'I can't eat this. Take is away!'

I somehow now see the tourist's wife stalking angrily out of the hotel, to get away from it all (without any shoes on), and, properly enough, the booklet seems to follow her course – first under 'Guides and Interpreters': 'You are asking too much.' 'I will not give you any more.' 'I shall call a policeman.' 'He can settle this affair.' Then under 'Inquiring the Way': 'I am lost.' 'I was looking for –' 'Someone robbed me.' 'That man robbed me.' 'That man is following me everywhere.' She rushes to 'The Hairdresser,' where, for a change, everything goes quite smoothly until: 'The water is too hot, you are scalding me!' Then she goes shopping, but there is no surcease: 'You have not given me the right change.' 'I bought this two days ago.' 'It doesn't work.' 'It is broken.' 'It is torn.' 'It doesn't fit me.' Then to a restaurant for a snack and a reviving cup of tea: 'This is not fresh.' 'This piece is too fat.' 'This doesn't smell very nice.' 'There is a mistake in the bill.' 'While I was dining someone has taken my purse.' 'I have left my glasses (my watch) (a ring) in the lavatory.' Madness has now come upon her and she rushes wildly out into the street. Her husband, I think, has at the same time plunged blindly out of the hotel to find her. We come then, quite naturally, to 'Accident,' which is calculated to keep the faint of heart – nay, the heart of oak – safely at home by his own fireside: 'There has been an accident!' 'Go and fetch a policeman quickly.' 'Is there a doctor near here?' 'Send for the ambulance.' 'He is seriously injured.' 'She has been run over.' 'He has been knocked down.' 'Someone has fallen in the water.' 'The ankle, the arm.' 'The back, a bone.' 'The face, the finger.' 'The foot, the head.' 'The knee, the leg.' 'The neck, the nose.' 'The wrist, the shoulder.' 'He has broken his arm.' 'He has broken his leg.' 'He has a sprained ankle.' 'He has a sprained wrist.' 'He is losing blood.' 'He has fainted.' 'He has lost consciousness.' 'He has burnt his face.' 'It is swollen.' 'It is bleeding.' 'Bring some cold water.' 'Help me to carry him.' (Apparently, you just let *her* lie there, while you attend to him – but, of course, she was merely run over, whereas he has taken a terrific tossing around.)

We next see the husband and wife back in their room at the dreary hotel, both in bed, and both obviously hysterical. This scene is entitled 'Illness': 'I am feeling very ill, send for the doctor.' 'I have pains in –' 'I have pains all over.' 'The back, the chest.' 'The ear, the head.' 'The eyes, the heart.' 'The joints, the kidneys.' 'The lungs, the stomach.' 'The throat, the tongue.' 'Put out your tongue.' 'The heart is affected.' 'I feel a pain here.' 'He is not sleeping well.' 'He cannot eat.' 'My stomach is out of order.' 'She is feverish.' 'I have caught a cold.' 'I have caught a chill.' 'He has a temperature.' 'I have a cough.' 'Will you give me a prescription?' 'What must I do?' 'Must I stay in bed?' 'I feel better.' 'When will you come and see me again?' 'Biliousness, rheumatism.' 'Insomnia, sunstroke.' 'Fainting, a fit.' 'Hoarseness, sore throat.' 'The medicine, the remedy.' 'A poultice, a draught.' 'A table-spoonful, a teaspoonful.' 'A sticking plaster, senna.' 'Iodine.' That last suicidal bleat for iodine is, to me, a masterful touch.

Our couple finally get on their feet again, for travelers are tough – they've got to be – but we see under the next heading, 'Common Words and Phrases,' that they are left forever punch-drunk and shattered: 'Can I help you?' 'Excuse me.' 'Carry on!' 'Look here!' 'Look down there!' 'Look up there!' 'Why, how?' 'When, where?' 'Because.' 'That's it!' 'It is too much, it is too dear.' 'It is very cheap.' 'Who, what, which?' 'Look out!' Those are Valkyries, one feels, riding around, and above, and under our unhappy husband and wife. The book sweeps on to a mad operatic ending of the tragedy, with all the strings and brasses and wood winds going full blast: 'Where are we going?' 'Where are you going?' 'Come quickly and see!' 'I shall call a policeman.' 'Bring a policeman!' 'I shall stay here.' 'Will you help me?' 'Help! Fire!' 'Who are you?' 'I don't know you.' 'I don't want to speak to you.' 'Leave me alone.' 'That will do.' 'You are mistaken.' 'It was not I.' 'I didn't do it.' 'I will give you nothing.' 'Go away now!' 'It has nothing to do with me.'

'Where should one apply?' 'What must I do?' 'What have I done?' 'I have done nothing.' 'I have already paid you.' 'I have paid you enough.' 'Let me pass!' 'Where is the British consulate?' The oboes take that last, despairing wail, and the curtain comes down.

The Catbird Seat

MR MARTIN bought the pack of Camels on Monday night in the most crowded cigar store on Broadway. It was theater time and seven or eight men were buying cigarettes. The clerk didn't even glance at Mr Martin, who put the pack in his overcoat pocket and went out. If any of the staff at F & S had seen him buy the cigarettes, they would have been astonished, for it was generally known that Mr Martin did not smoke, and never had. No one saw him.

It was just a week to the day since Mr Martin had decided to rub out Mrs Ulgine Barrows. The term 'rub out' pleased him because it suggested nothing more than the correction of an error – in this case an error of Mr Fitweiler. Mr Martin had spent each night of the past week working out his plan and examining it. As he walked home now he went over it again. For the hundredth time he resented the element of imprecision, the margin of guesswork that entered into the business. The project as he had worked it out was casual and bold, the risks were considerable. Something might go wrong anywhere along the line. And therein lay the cunning of his scheme. No one would ever see in it the cautious, painstaking hand of Erwin Martin, head of the filing department at F & S, of whom Mr Fitweiler had once said,

'Man is fallible but Martin isn't.' No one would see his hand, that is, unless it were caught in the act.

Sitting in his apartment, drinking a glass of milk, Mr Martin reviewed his case against Mrs Ulgine Barrows, as he had every night for seven nights. He began at the beginning. Her quacking voice and braying laugh had first profaned the halls of F & S on March 7, 1941 (Mr Martin had a head for dates). Old Roberts, the personnel chief, had introduced her as the newly appointed special adviser to the president of the firm, Mr Fitweiler. The woman had appalled Mr Martin instantly, but he hadn't shown it. He had given her his dry hand, a look of studious concentration, and a faint smile. 'Well,' she said, looking at the papers on his desk, 'are you lifting the oxcart out of the ditch?' As Mr Martin recalled that moment, over his milk, he squirmed slightly. He must keep his mind on her crimes as a special adviser, not on her peccadillos as a personality. This he found difficult to do, in spite of entering an objection and sustaining it. The faults of the woman as a woman kept chattering on in his mind like an unruly witness. She had, for almost two years now, baited him. In the halls, in the elevator, even in his own office, into which she romped now and then like a circus horse, she was constantly shouting these silly questions at him. 'Are you lifting the oxcart out of the ditch? Are you tearing up the pea patch? Are you hollering down the rain barrel? Are you scraping around the bottom of the pickle barrel? Are you sitting in the catbird seat?'

It was Joey Hart, one of Mr Martin's two assistants, who had explained what the gibberish meant. 'She must be a Dodger fan,' he had said. 'Red Barber announces the Dodger games over the radio and he uses those expressions – picked 'em up down South.' Joey had gone on to explain one or two. 'Tearing up the pea patch' meant going on a rampage; 'sitting in the catbird seat' meant sitting pretty, like a batter with three balls and no strikes on him. Mr Martin dismissed all this with an effort. It had been annoying, it had driven him near to distraction, but he was too solid a man to be moved to murder by anything so childish. It was fortunate, he reflected as he passed on to the important charges against Mrs Barrows, that he had stood up under it so well. He had maintained always an outward appearance of polite tolerance. 'Why, I even believe you like the woman,' Miss Paird, his other assistant, had once said to him. He had simply smiled.

A gavel rapped in Mr Martin's mind and the case proper was resumed. Mrs Ulgine Barrows stood charged with willful, blatant, and persistent attempts to destroy the efficiency and system of F & S. It was competent, material, and relevant to review her advent and rise to power. Mr Martin had got the story from Miss Paird, who seemed always able to find things out. According to her, Mrs Barrows had met Mr Fitweiler at a party, where she had rescued him from the embraces of a powerfully built drunken man who had mistaken the president of F & S for a famous retired Middle Western football coach. She had led him to a sofa and somehow worked upon him a monstrous magic. The aging gentleman had jumped to the conclusion there and then that this was a woman of singular attainments, equipped to bring out the best in him and in the firm. A week later he had introduced her into F &

S as his special adviser. On that day confusion got its foot in the door. After Miss Tyson, Mr Brundage, and Mr Bartlett had been fired and Mr Munson had taken his hat and stalked out, mailing in his resignation later, old Roberts had been emboldened to speak to Mr Fitweiler. He mentioned that Mr Munson's department had been 'a little disrupted' and hadn't they perhaps better resume the old system there?' Mr Fitweiler had said certainly not. He had the greatest faith in Mrs Barrow's ideas. 'They require a little seasoning, a little seasoning, is all,' he had added. Mr Roberts had given it up. Mr Martin reviewed in detail all the changes wrought by Mrs Barrows. She had begun chipping at the cornices of the firm's edifice and now she was swinging at the foundation stones with a pickaxe.

Mr Martin came now, in his summing up, to the afternoon of Monday, November 2, 1942 – just one week ago. On that day, at 3 p.m., Mrs Barrows had bounced into his office. 'Boo!' she had yelled. 'Are you scraping around the bottom of the pickle barrel?' Mr Martin had looked at her from under his green eyeshade, saying nothing. She had begun to wander about the office, taking it in with her great, popping eyes. 'Do you really need *all* these filing cabinets?' she had demanded suddenly. Mr Martin's heart had jumped. 'Each of these files,' he had said, keeping his voice even, 'plays an indispensable part in the system of F & S.' She had brayed at him. 'Well, don't tear up the pea patch!' and gone to the door. From there she had bawled, 'But you sure have got a lot of fine scrap in here!' Mr Martin could no longer doubt that the finger was on his beloved department. Her pickaxe was on the upswing, poised for the first blow. It had not come yet; he had received no blue memo from the enchanted Mr Fitweiler bearing non-sensical instructions deriving from the obscene woman. But there was no doubt in Mr Martin's mind that one would be forthcoming. He must act quickly. Already a precious week had gone by. Mr Martin stood up in his living room, still holding his milk glass. 'Gentlemen of the jury,' he said to himself, 'I demand the death penalty for this horrible person.'

The next day Mr Martin followed his routine, as usual. He polished his glasses more often and once sharpened an already sharp pencil, but not even Miss Paird noticed. Only once did he catch sight of his victim; she swept past him in the hall with a patronizing 'Hi!' At five-thirty he walked home, as usual, and had a glass of milk, as usual. He had never drunk anything stronger in his life – unless you could count ginger ale. The late Sam Schlosser, the S of F & S, had praised Mr Martin at a staff meeting several years before for his temperate habits. 'Our most efficient worker neither drinks nor smokes,' he had said. 'The results speak for themselves.' Mr Fitweiler had sat by, nodding approval.

Mr Martin was still thinking about that red-letter day as he walked over to the Schrafft's on Fifth Avenue near Forty-sixth Street. He got there, as he always did, at eight o'clock. He finished his dinner and the financial page of the *Sun* at a quarter to nine, as he always did. It was his custom after dinner to take a walk. This time he walked down Fifth Avenue at a casual pace. His gloved hands felt moist and warm, his forehead cold. He transferred the Camels from his overcoat to a jacket pocket. He wondered, as he did so, if they did not represent an unnecessary note of strain. Mrs Barrows smoked only Luckies. It was his idea to puff a few puffs on a Camel (after the rubbing-out), stub it out in the ashtray holding her lipstick-stained Luckies, and thus drag a small red herring across the trail. Perhaps it was not a good idea. It would take time. He might even choke, too loudly.

Mr Martin had never seen the house on West Twelfth Street where Mrs Barrows lived, but he had a clear enough picture of it. Fortunately, she had bragged to everybody about her ducky first-floor apartment in the perfectly darling three-story red-brick. There would be no doorman or other attendants; just the tenants of the second and third floors. As he walked along, Mr Martin realized that he would get there before nine-thirty. He had considered walking north on Fifth Avenue from Schrafft's to a point from which it would take him until ten o'clock to reach the house. At that hour people were less likely to be coming in or going out. But the procedure would have made an awkward loop in the straight thread of the casualness, and he had abandoned it. It was impossible to figure when people would be entering or leaving the house, anyway. There was a great risk at any hour. If he ran into anybody, he would simply have to place the rubbing-out of Ulgine Barrows in the inactive file forever. The same thing would hold true if there were someone in her apartment. In that case he would just say that he had been passing by, recognized her charming house and thought to drop in.

It was eighteen minutes after nine when Mr Martin

turned into Twelfth Street. A man passed him, and a man and a woman talking. There was no one within fifty paces when he came to the house, halfway down the block. He was up the steps and in the small vestibule in no time, pressing the bell under the card that said 'Mrs Ulgine Barrows.' When the clicking in the lock started, he jumped forward against the door. He got inside fast, closing the door behind him. A bulb in a lantern hung from the hall ceiling on a chain seemed to give a monstrously bright light. There was nobody on the stair, which went up ahead of him along the left wall. A door opened down the hall in the wall on the right. He went toward it swiftly, on tiptoe.

'Well, for God's sake, look who's here!' bawled Mrs. Barrows, and her braying laugh rang out like the report of a shotgun. He rushed past her like a football tackle, bumping her. 'Hey, quit shoving!' she said, closing the door behind them. They were in her living room, which seemed to Mr Martin to be lighted by a hundred lamps. 'What's after you?' she said. 'You're as jumpy as a goat.' He found he was unable to speak. His heart was wheezing in his throat. 'I – yes,' he finally brought out. She was jabbering and laughing as she started to help him off with his coat. 'No, no,' he said. 'I'll put it here.' He took it off and put it on a chair near the door. 'Your hat and gloves, too,' she said. 'You're in a lady's house.' He put his hat on top of the coat. Mrs Barrows seemed larger than he had thought. He kept his gloves on. 'I was passing by,' he said. 'I recognized – is there anyone here?' She laughed louder than ever. 'No,' she said, 'we're all alone. You're as white as a sheet, you funny man. Whatever *has* come over you? I'll mix you a toddy.' She started toward a door across the room. 'Scotch-and-soda be all right? But say, you don't drink, do you?' She turned and gave him her amused look. Mr Martin pulled himself together. 'Scotch-and-soda will be all right,' he heard himself say. He could hear her laughing in the kitchen.

Mr Martin looked quickly around the living room, for the weapon. He had counted on finding one there. There were andirons and a poker and something in a corner that looked like an Indian club. None of them would do. It couldn't be that way. He began to pace around. He came to a desk. On it lay a metal paper knife with an ornate handle. Would it be sharp enough? He reached for it and knocked over a small brass jar. Stamps spilled out of it and it fell to the floor with a clatter. 'Hey,' Mrs Barrows yelled from the kitchen, 'are you tearing up the pea patch?' Mr Martin gave a strange laugh. Picking up the knife, he tried its point against his left wrist. It was blunt. It wouldn't do.

When Mrs Barrows reappeared, carrying two highballs, Mr Martin, standing there with his gloves on, became acutely conscious of the fantasy he had wrought. Cigarettes in his pocket, a drink prepared for him – it was all too grossly improbable. It was more than that; it was impossible. Somewhere in the back of his mind a vague idea stirred, sprouted. 'For heaven's sake, take off those gloves,' said Mrs Barrows. 'I always wear them in the house,' said Mr Martin. The idea began to bloom, strange and wonderful. She put the glasses on a coffee table in front of a sofa and sat on the sofa. 'Come over here, you odd little man,' she said. Mr Martin went over and sat beside her. It was difficult getting a cigarette out of the pack of Camels, but he managed it. She held a match for him, laughing. 'Well,' she said, handing him his drink, 'this is perfectly marvelous. You with a drink and a cigarette.'

Mr Martin puffed, not too awkwardly, and took a gulp of the highball. 'I drink and smoke all the time,' he said. He clinked his glass against hers. 'Here's nuts to that old windbag, Fitweiler,' he said, and gulped again. The stuff tasted awful, but he made no grimace. 'Really, Mr Martin,' she said, her voice and posture changing, 'you are insulting our employer.' Mrs Barrows was now special adviser to the president. 'I am preparing a bomb,' said Mr Martin, 'which will blow the old goat higher than hell.' He had only had a little of the drink, which was not strong. It couldn't be that. 'Do you take dope or something?' Mrs Barrows asked coldly. 'Heroin,' said Mr Martin. 'I'll be coked to the gills when I bump that old buzzard off.' 'Mr Martin!' she shouted, getting to her feet. 'That will be all of that. You must go at once.' Mr Martin took another swallow of his drink. He tapped his cigarette out in the ashtray and put the pack of Camels on the coffee table. Then he got up. She stood glaring at him. He walked over and put on his hat and coat. 'Not a word about this,' he said, and laid an index finger against his lips. All Mrs Barrows could bring out was 'Really!' Mr Martin put his hand on the doorknob. 'I'm sitting in the catbird seat,' he said. He stuck his tongue out at her and left. Nobody saw him go.

Mr Martin got to his apartment, well before eleven. No one saw him go in. He had two glasses of milk after brushing his teeth, and he felt elated. It wasn't tipsiness, because he hadn't been tipsy. Anyway, the walk had worn off all the effects of the whisky. He got in bed and read a magazine for a while. He was asleep before midnight.

Mr Martin got to the office at eight-thirty the next morning, as usual. At a quarter to nine, Ulgine Barrows, who had never before arrived at work before ten, swept into his office. 'I'm reporting to Mr Fitweiler now!' she shouted. 'If he turns you over to the police, it's no more than you deserve!' Mr Martin gave her a look of shocked surprise. 'I beg your pardon?' he said. Mrs Barrows snorted and bounced out of the room, leaving Miss Paird and Joey Hart staring after her. 'What's the matter with that old devil now?' asked Miss Paird. 'I have no idea,' said Mr Martin, resuming his work. The other two looked at him and then at each other. Miss Paird got up and went out. She walked slowly past the closed door of Mr Fitweiler's office. Mrs Barrows was yelling inside, but she was not braying. Miss Paird could not hear what the woman was saying. She went back to her desk.

Forty-five minutes later, Mrs. Barrows left the president's office and went into her own, shutting the door. It wasn't until half an hour later that Mr Fitweiler sent for Mr Martin. The head of the filing department, neat, quiet, attentive, stood in front of the old man's desk. Mr Fitweiler was pale and nervous. He took his glasses off and twiddled them. He made a small, bruffing sound in his throat. 'Martin,' he said, 'you have been with us more than twenty years.' 'Twenty-two sir,' said Mr Martin. 'In that time,' pursued the president, 'you work and your – uh – manner have been exemplary.' 'I trust so, sir,' said Mr Martin. 'I have understood, Martin,' said Mr Fitweiler, 'that you have never taken a drink or smoked.' 'That is correct, sir,' said Mr Martin. 'Ah, yes.' Mr Fitweiler polished his glasses. 'You may describe what you did after leaving the office yesterday, Martin,' he said. Mr Martin allowed less than a second for his bewildered pause. 'Certainly, sir,' he said. 'I walked home. Then I went to Schrafft's for dinner. Afterward I walked home again. I went to bed early, sir, and read a magazine for a while. I was asleep before eleven.' 'Ah, yes,' said Mr Fitweiler again. He was silent for a moment, searching for the proper words to say to the head of the filing department. 'Mrs Barrows,' he said finally, 'Mrs Barrows has worked hard, Martin, very hard. It grieves me to report that she has suffered a severe breakdown. It has taken the form of a persecution complex accompanied by distressing hallucinations.' 'I am very sorry, sir,' said Mr Martin. 'Mrs Barrows is under the delusion,' continued Mr Fitweiler, 'that you visited her last evening and behaved yourself in an – uh – unseemly manner.' He raised his hand to silence Mr Martin's little pained outcry. 'It is the nature of these psychological diseases,' Mr Fitweiler said, 'to fix upon the least likely and most innocent party as the – uh – source of persecution. These matters are not for the lay mind to grasp, Martin. I've just had my psychiatrist, Dr Fitch, on the phone. He would not, of course, commit himself, but he made enough generalizations to substantiate my suspicious. I suggested to Mrs Barrows when she had completed her – uh – story to me this morning, that she visit Dr Fitch, for I suspected a condition at once. She flew,

I regret to say, into a rage, and demanded – uh – requested that I call you on the carpet. You may not know, Martin, but Mrs Barrows had planned a reorganization of your department – subject to my approval, of course, subject to my approval. This brought you, rather than anyone else, to her mind – but again that is a phenomenon for Dr Fitch and not for us. So, Martin, I am afraid Mrs Barrows' usefulness here is at an end.' 'I'm dreadfully sorry, sir,' said Mr Martin.

It was at this point that the door to the office flew open with the suddenness of a gas-main explosion and Mrs Barrows catapulted through it. 'Is the little rat trying to deny it?' she screamed. 'He can't get away with that!' Mr Martin got up and moved discreetly to a point beside Mr Fitweiler's chair. 'You drank and smoked at my apartment,' she bawled at Mr Martin, 'and you know it! You called Mr Fitweiler an old windbag and said you were going to blow him up when you got choked to the gills on your heroin!' She stopped yelling to catch her breath and a new glint came into her popping eyes. 'If you weren't such a drab, ordinary little man,' she said, 'I'd think you'd planned it all. Sticking your tongue out at me, saying you were sitting in the catbird seat, because you thought no one would believe me when I told it! My God, it's really too perfect!' she brayed loudly and hysterically, and the fury was on her again. She glared at Mr Fitweiler. 'Can't you see how he has tricked us, you old fool? Can't you see his little game?' But Mr Fitweiler had been surreptitiously pressing all the buttons under the top of his desk and employees for F & S began pouring into the room. 'Stockton,' said Mr Fitweiler, 'you and Fishbein will take Mrs Barrows to her home. Mrs

Powell, you will go with them.' Stockton, who had played a little football in high school, blocked Mrs Barrows as she made for Mr Martin. It took him and Fishbein together to force her out of the door into the hall, crowded with stenographers and office boys. She was still screaming imprecations at Mr Martin, tangled and contradictory imprecations. The hubbub finally died out down the corridor.

'I regret that this has happened,' said Mr Fitweiler. 'I shall ask you to dismiss it from your mind Martin.' 'Yes, sir,' said Mr Martin, anticipating his chief's 'That will be all' by moving to the door. 'I will dismiss it.' He went out and shut the door, and his step was light and quick in the hall. When he entered his department he had slowed down to his customary gait, and he walked quietly across the room to the W20 file, wearing a look of studious concentration.

Look Homeward, Jeannie

The moot and momentous question as to whether lost dogs have the mysterious power of being able to get back home from distant places over strange terrain has been argued for years by dog owners, dog haters, and other persons who really do not know much about the matter. Mr Bergen Evans in his book, 'The Natural History of Nonsense,' flatly sides with the cynics who believe that the lost dog doesn't have any more idea where he is than a babe in the woods. 'Like pigeons,' wrote Mr Evans, 'dogs are thought to have a supernatural ability to find their way home across hundreds, even thousands of miles of strange terrain. The newspapers are full of stories of dogs who have miraculously turned up at the doorsteps of baffled masters who had abandoned them afar. Against these stories, however, can be set the lost and found columns of the same papers, which in almost every issue carry offers of rewards for the recovery of dogs that, apparently, couldn't find their way back from the next block.' Mr Evans, you see, touches on this difficult and absorbing subject in the uneasy manner of a minister caught alone in a parlor with an irritable schnauzer.

Now I don't actually know any more than Mr Evans does about the dogs that are supposed to return from strange, distant places as surely as an Indian scout or a locomotive engineer, but I am not prepared to write them off as fantasy on the strength of armchair argument. Skepticism is a useful tool of the inquisitive mind, but it is scarcely a method of investigation. I would like to see an expert reporter, like Alva Johnston or Meyer Berger, set out on the trail of a homing dog and see what he would find.

I happen to have a few haphazard clippings on the fascinating subject but they are unsupported, as always, by convincing proof of any kind. The most interesting case is that of Bosco, a small dog who is reported to have returned to his house in Knoxville, Tenn., in the winter of 1944 from Glendale, Calif., thus setting what is probably the world's distance record for the event, twenty-three hundred miles in seven months. His story is recorded in a book called 'Just a Mutt,' by Eldon Roark, a columnist on *The Memphis Press-Scimitar*. Mr Roark says he got his tip on the story from Bert Vincent of *The Knoxville News-Sentinel*, but in a letter to me Mr Vincent says he has some doubts of the truth of the long trek through towns and cities and over rivers and deserts.

The dog belonged to a family named Flanigan and Mr Vincent does not question the sincerity of their belief that the dog who turned up on their porch one day was, in fact, Bosco come home. The dog bore no collar or license, however, and identification had to be made on the tricky basis of markings and behavior. The long-distance record of Bosco must be reluctantly set down as a case that would stand up only in a court of lore.

Far-traveling dogs have become so common that jaded

editors are inclined to turn their activities over to the society editors, and we may expect before long to encounter such items as this: 'Rex, a bull terrier, owned by Mr and Mrs Charles L. Thompson of this city, returned to his home at 2334 Maybury Avenue yesterday, after a four months' trip from Florida where he was lost last February. Mr and Mrs Thompson's daughter, Alice Louise, is expected home to-morrow from Shipley, to spend the summer vacation.'

Incidentally, and just for the sake of a fair record, my two most recent clippings on the Long Trek deal with cats, as follows: Kit-Kat, Lake Tahoe to Long Beach, Calif., 525 miles; Mr Black, Stamford, Conn., to Atlanta, Ga., 1,000 miles.

The homing dog reached apotheosis a few years ago when 'Lassie Come Home' portrayed a collie returning to its young master over miles of wild and unfamiliar terrain in darkness and in storm. This million-dollar testament of faith, a kind of unconscious memorial to the late Albert Payson Terhune, may possibly be what inspired Bergen Evans' slighting remarks.

I suspect that Professor Evans has not owned a dog since Brownie was run over by the Chalmers. In the presence of the 'lost' dog in the next block, he is clearly on insecure ground. He assumes that the dog does not come back from the next block because it can't find its way. If this reasoning were applied to the thousands of men who disappear from their homes every year, it would exonerate them of every flaw except disorientation, and this is too facile an explanation for man or beast. Prince, the dog, has just as many reasons for getting and staying the hell out as George, the husband: an attractive female, merry companions, change

of routine, words of praise, small attentions, new horizons, an easing of discipline. The dog that does not come home is too large a field of research for one investigator, and so I will confine myself to the case history of Jeannie.

Jeannie was a small Scottish terrier whose nature and behavior I observed closely over a period of years. She had no show points to speak of. Her jaw was skimpy, her haunches frail, her forelegs slightly bowed. She thought dimly and her coordination was only fair. Even in repose she had the strained, uncomfortable appearance of a woman on a bicycle.

Jeannie adjusted slowly and reluctantly to everything, including weather. Rain was a hand raised against her personally, snow a portent of evil, thunder the end of the world. She sniffed even the balmiest breeze with an air of apprehension, as if it warned of the approach of a monster at least as large as a bus.

Jeannie did everything the hard way, digging with one paw at a time, shoving out of screen doors sideways, delivering pups on the floor of a closet completely covered with shoes. When she was six months old, she tried to bury a bone in the second edition of *The New York Times*, pushing confidently and futilely at the newsprint with her muzzle. She developed a persistent troubled frown which gave her the expression of someone who is trying to repair a watch with his gloves on.

Jeannie spent the first two years of her life in the city, where her outdoor experiences were confined to trips around the block. When she was taken to the country to live, she clung to the hearth for several weeks, poking her nose out now and then for a dismaying glimpse of what she considered to be God's great Scottie trap. The scent of lawn moles and the scurry of squirrels brought her out into the yard finally for tentative explorations, but it was a long time before she followed the woodchuck's trail up to the edge of the woods.

Within a few months Jeannie took to leaving the house when the sun came up and returning when it began to get dark. Her outings seemed to be good for her. She began to look sleek, fat, smug, and at the same time pleasantly puzzled, like a woman who finds more money in her handbag than she thought was there. I decided to follow her discreetly one day, and she led me a difficult four-mile chase to where a large group of summer people occupied a row of cottages near a lake. Jeannie, it came out, was the camp mascot. She had muzzled in, and for some time had been spending her days shaking down the cottagers for hamburgers, fried potatoes, cake and marshmallows. They wondered where the cute little dog came from in the morning and where she went at night.

Jeannie had won them over with her only trick. She could sit up, not easily, but with amusing effort, placing her right forefoot on a log or stone, and pushing. Her sitting-up stance was teetery and precarious, but if she fell over on her back or side, she was rewarded just the same, if not, indeed, even more bountifully. She couldn't lose. The camp was a pushover.

Little old One Trick had a slow mind, but she gradually figured out that the long trip home after her orgies was a waste of time, an unnecessary loop in her new economy. Oh, she knew the way back all right, Evans – by what improbable system of landmarks I could never guess – but when she got home there was no payoff except a plain wholesome meal once a day. That was all right for young dogs and very old dogs and spaniels, but not for a terrier who had struck it rich over the hills. She took to staying away for days at a time. I would have to go and get her in the car and bring her back.

One day, the summer people, out for a hike, brought her home themselves, and Jeannie realized the game was up, for the campers obviously believed in what was, to her, the outworn principle of legal ownership. To her dismay they showed themselves to be believers in one-man loyalty, a virtue which Jeannie had outgrown. The next time I drove to the camp to get her she wasn't there. I found out finally from the man who delivered the mail where she was. 'Your little dog is on the other side of the lake,' he said. 'She's stayin' with a school teacher in a cottage the other side of the lake.' I found her easily enough.

The school teacher, I learned, had opened her door one morning to discover a small Scottie sitting up in the front yard, begging. The cute little visitor had proceeded to take her new hostess for three meals a day, topped off now and then with chocolates. But I had located her hiding place, and the next time she disappeared from home she moved on to fresh fields. 'Your little dog's stayin' with some folks over near Danbury,' the mailman told me a week later. He explained how to get to the house. 'The hell with it,' I said, but a few hours later I got in the car and went after her, anyway.

She was lying on the front porch of her current home in a posture of truculent possession. When I stopped the car at the curb she charged vociferously down the steps, not to greet the master, but to challenge a trespasser. When she got close enough to recognize me, her belligerence sagged. 'Better luck next time,' I said, coldly. I opened the door and she climbed slowly into the car and up on to the sear beside me. We both stared straight ahead all the way home.

Jeannie was a lost dog, lost in another way than Evans understands. There wasn't anything to do about it. After all, I had my own life to live. Before long I would have had to follow her as far as Stamford or Darien or wherever the gravy happened to be thickest and the clover sweetest. 'Your little dog' – the mailman began a few days later. 'I know,' I said, 'thanks,' and went back into the house. She came home of her own accord about three weeks later and I think she actually made an effort to adjust herself to her real home. It was too late, though.

When Jeannie died, at the age of nine, possibly of a surfeit of Page & Shaw's, I got a very nice letter from the people she was living with at the time.

A Friend of the Earth

WHEN MY mother was in Ludlow, Connecticut, on one of her visits ten years ago, she took a fancy to Zeph Leggin – practically everybody did except old Miss Eldon and me – and he gave her a picture of himself. People were always taking pictures of Zeph, in one or another of his favorite, and locally famous, poses – playing his harmonica, whittling, drowsing in a chair against the wall of his shack, eating a hard-boiled egg. The most celebrated of the egg studies shows him on his thirty-sixth the day he ate three dozen at a sitting, on a bet.

Zeph Leggin was a character in the classic mould, a lazy rustic philosopher, whose comic criticism of the futility of action and accomplishment made up, I was told, for his inability to complete a task, his failure to show up on time (or, sometimes, even at all), his genius at waggish confusion, and his light regard for the convenience of others. 'Wait 'til you meet Zeph Leggin,' an ecstatic neighbor said to me just after I came to Ludlow. 'He'll drive you nuts, the old rascal, but you'll love him. We all do – except Miss Eldon. We always hire him for odd jobs. Used to be a master carpenter, they say, but now he doesn't give a good goddam. Funniest guy you ever heard talk, though. "Lost my wife ten years ago," he'll say to you. Play it straight. Say, "That's too bad!" "Yep," he'll tell you, "lost her in a drygoods store – I slipped out the back door." Ha ha ha!'

For such bewildered foreign eyes as may fall upon these lines, I should perhaps explain that ours is a good-natured commonwealth of straight men and stooges, willing and eager to let a wall crumble, or a roof sag, or a pipe freeze if the vandal responsible for the trouble has a Will Rogers grin, a soft drawl, and a dry way of saying things. There must be something grave the matter with me. From the moment I set eyes on Ephraim J. (Zeph) Leggin, I wanted to poke him in the nose. For the sake of a fair record, I must report that Zeph took an instant dislike to me, too. Zeph was a-sittin' in front of his shack and a-playin' his mouth organ – he called it Ole Maria, I heard later – when Paul Morton, the neighbor I quoted earlier, led me up to him one afternoon. I was presented to Zeph Leggin. It was regarded as an honor, I had been told, if he stopped playing, opened his eyes, and deigned to speak. 'Zeph, I want you to meet Mr Thurber,' said Paul. Zeph kept right on playing. 'He's come to Ludlow to live – a new neighbor of ours,' Paul went on. Zeph finished another bar of 'Nellie Gray' and looked up – at Paul, not at me. 'He a married man?' he asked. That nettled me. He hadn't acknowledged the introduction by so much as a nod, and I didn't like the practiced twinkle in his eye. I could see what was coming, and I beat him to the punch. It was small of me, I suppose, but I offer the purely human excuse that we had come to dislike each other in the first few seconds. 'I lost my wife ten years ago,' I heard myself saying in a strained, chill tone. The twinkle in Zeph's eyes died and a hard look took its place. With our rapiers crossed and clashing, we searched for each other's gullet. He was shrewd, all right, and not slow of mind. He knew that I must have been tipped off to this opening gambit of his. He threw a quick, baleful glance at Paul, who he must have figured was the tattle-tale. 'Lost her in a drygoods store, eh?' Zeph asked me, and the Devil took hold of my tongue. 'She died,' I said coldly, and it almost brought Zeph up out of his tilted chair. Then he saw the astonished look that Paul gave me, and he knew I was trying to knock his foil from his hand by an inexcusable trick. 'Now, that's too bad, Bub,' he said nastily. 'Come on, Jim, let's go,' said Paul. 'I want to show you my studio.' But Zeph and I were glaring at each other. 'Yes, she died laughing,' I said, 'at a back-woods Voltaire.' 'Come on, Jim, for God's sake,' said Paul, taking me by the arm. Zeph closed his eyes, leaned back, and began to play 'Nellie Gray' again on his harmonica. The bargain of our enmity was sealed.

The only thing Miss Eldon and I had in common, I found out later, was our lonely immunity to the magic spell of Zeph Leggin, and since she was a hard and hollow old lady, there were dark moments when I felt I must belong to the wrong school of thought in the case of the Ludlow minstrel. Miss Eldon had not spoken to Zeph, or allowed him on her premises, since the day of the Great Insult, May 16th, 1934. She kept all dates, important and otherwise, neatly arranged in the back of her mind, along with her fine collection of old platitudes. On the day in question, she had summoned Zeph to her house – or, rather, she had summoned him a week before, and he had finally shown up on the sixteenth. She told him that her problem was beetles in the pantry. Zeph had a considerable reputation as an exterminator. He would never tell what it was that he used, except to say that the secret formula had been given to his great-grandmother by a sick Indian she had nursed back to health. 'They ain't beetles in your pantry, Ma'am,' said Zeph. 'They's cockroaches.' Miss Eldon's nose expressed disgust at the man's frank vulgarity. 'Well, whatever they are,' she said, 'they're as big as mice.' She had asked for it, she had walked right into it. Zeph's eyes twinkled and he put on his Sunday drawl. 'The only way to get rid of cockroaches big as mice, Ma'am,' he said, 'is to stop drinkin'.' She ordered him out of the house, and he shambled away playing 'Polly Wolly Doodle' on his harmonica. 'The man is gross,' she told me. I had some difficulty maintaining an expression of grave disapproval of the gross man, but I managed it.

The grinning face of Zeph Leggin hung over my house in Ludlow like a moon. He didn't come around during the first couple of weeks, and I didn't send for him, although a number of chores needed doing, but his face was always rising in my consciousness, bland and bright and impudent, and I kept hearing the mischievous music of Ole Maria playing on the edges of my mind. The fellow had called me Bub and I don't get over such things easily. Somewhere, I felt, he was thinking up gags, or planning pranks to disconcert me. Paul Morton thought I was acting like a child about the town comic, especially when he found out that I couldn't use the studio behind the house until several rotted boards in the floor were replaced. 'Why don't you get

Zeph over to fix it?' Paul wanted to know. It was a foolish question and I gave him a foolish answer. 'He insulted the memory of my dead wife,' I said. Paul was amazed. '*You* started that,' he said. 'You spoiled his little joke about the drygoods store, and got *me* in bad – he knew I had told you about it.' 'I'm sorry,' I said, 'but even if it hadn't happened, Leggin and I would never get along. Each of us wishes the other were dead. It takes all kinds of people to make up a world, Paul – the seasick sailor, the surgeon who faints at the sight of blood, and the Man Who Hated Leggin, as I am destined to be known after I'm gone. If Zeph were the last—' 'Nuts,' said Paul, and went away.

It was about ten days later that I heard the sounds of someone moving around in the studio. I went out to investigate. It was Zeph. He was standing with his back to me, studying the rotted floor boards, and although he must have heard me come in, he didn't turn around. 'Fella goes to this grocery store,' he said over his shoulder, 'and sez to the man, "What you got in the shape of bananas?" "Cucumbers," sez the man.' He tapped one of the boards with his shoe and turned around slowly. 'What you got in the shape of tool?' he asked. I wasn't going to play any games with the old rascal. 'I rented this house furnished,' I told him, 'I haven't had time to find out where everything is. I thought you had tools of your own.' He gave me a twinkle. 'Won't know about that 'til I get back home,' he said. He took it for granted that the job of fixing the floor, like all other tasks of the kind, was his by inalienable right and I decided to let it go at that. 'There ought to be a toolbox somewhere in the house,' I said. He gave me the grin. 'Twon't come to *us*,' he told me. 'We'll have to go to *it*.' On the way out of the studio, Zeph stopped at a table and picked up a flashlight that lay on it. He clicked it several times and then said, 'Needs new batteries. I'll be goin' by Barton's store in Danbury this afternoon. Want me to take it along?' I told him that would be fine and thanked him, and he put the flashlight in his pocket. I can't remember now where we found the saw, but the search lasted a good twenty minutes. Zeph examined it carefully and then put it down. 'Can't use it,' he said. 'Left-handed saw.' I studied it for a few moments. 'I guess you'll have to bring your own, then,' I said. He frowned. 'Job a work comes a little higher iffen I furnish my own tools,' he announced. I turned without saying anything and he led the way out of the house. 'When can you get at the job?' I asked him. He looked at the sky and then held out one hand, as if testing the quality of the air. 'Bit dry for sawin',' he said finally, but he couldn't trap me into any comment on this. 'There are some sound planks in one corner of the studio,' I said. 'Did you see them?' Zeph's grin crinkled the corners of his eyes. 'I *saw* 'em,' he said. We both turned away at the same moment and went about our business, or, to be more exact, I went about mine.

It rained that night and there were showers off and on for several days. On the fourth day after Zeph's visit, I ran into him at the post office. 'Why haven't you been over to fix the floor?' I demanded. Zeph unwrapped a stick of gum with great care, put it in his mouth, and chewed for half a minute. 'Twant sawin' weather,' he said. Paul Morton would have laughed his head off and I should have let it ride, but I didn't. 'Twar,' I snarled loudly, and several of my neighbors turned and stared. I decided I might just as well break with Leggin for good then and there. 'I don't think you can tell a hawk from a handsaw,' I said sharply. I told you before that his mind was quick enough. He squinted at me for only a few seconds. 'You lay 'em out in the weather,' he said. 'The one that rusts is the handsaw.' Several people who had listened to this exchange laughed loudly. Old Zeph was in form. One of them slapped him on the back. I left the post office and walked home muttering to myself. 'Mail?' said my wife when I walked into the living room. It *was* mail of a kind – three letters I had taken to the post office and forgotten to put in the slot.

Zeph fixed the studio floor about two weeks later. I heard him sawing and nailing, with long intervals of silence in between, but I didn't go out to the studio to see how he was getting along. I confess there was more to this than my instantaneous annoyance at the sight of the man. I was afraid of his tongue. He had thrown me over his shoulder, easily and in public. He was in the studio most of the afternoon, and if I had hoped that he would go away without dropping in on me, I was doomed, as the saying goes, to disappointment. Zeph never knocked on anybody's door. He just opened it and came in. He found me in the living room. 'Job's done,' he said. 'So soon?' I snapped. He pulled the flashlight out of his pocket, walked over to my chair, and handed it to me. 'Thanks,' I said unamiably. 'Send me a bill for the carpentry.' 'Got it right here,' said Zeph, and he handed me a slip of paper. I glanced at it, and it seemed reasonable enough. Then I clicked the flashlight. It didn't work. 'It doesn't work,' I told him. He twinkled and grinned. 'Needs new batteries,' he said. I should have known better. I should have said nothing. But once again I walked into his little trap. 'You said you would take it to Barton's and have it fixed,' I told him. His eyes crinkled. 'Nope,' he said. 'Told you I was goin' by, didn't say nothin' about stoppin' in.' That was too much for me. I brought the flashlight down with a great force on the edge of a table and smashed it to bits. Then I turned slowly to Zeph Leggin, my eyebrows up, in feigned astonishment. 'Defective,' I said coldly. Zeph took his harmonica out of his pocket and rubbed it with a palm of his hand. He had lost the twinkle and the grin. It was a moment rare, perhaps unique, in the life of the great philosopher. Zeph Leggin couldn't think of anything to say. He walked out of the room playing 'Nellie Grey,' and that was the last time we ever spoke to each other. I got a man named Larkin, from Danbury, whenever anything around the house needed fixing.

I think it was in September that the Ludlow Men's Forum decided to ask Zeph Leggin to be the principal speaker at their monthly meeting. I saw the announcement in the Ludlow *Journal*. It said that Ephraim Leggin, Ludlow's most beloved citizen, had consented to address his neighbors and to share with them his rich and salty wisdom and his profound knowledge of life. The title of his talk, the *Journal* said, was 'A Friend of the Earth.' The Forum meetings were held in the small chapel across the street from the Congregational Church. There were about forty of us present when, after the reading of the minutes of the previous meeting and the reports of various chairmen of committees, the smiling Paul Morton stood up to introduce the speaker of the evening. It was an introduction dripping with marmalade and ornamented with flowers, and everybody loved it and everybody laughed and applauded as Zeph got slowly to his feet. I had seen him only once or twice in passing since the incident of the shattered flashlight. I had felt ashamed about that show of temper and I hadn't even told my wife that I had broken the lamp deliberately. Zeph let his eyes roam about the room and they fell upon me at last, in a chair near the wall in a row at the back.

'Neighbors,' began Zeph, 'I ain't always bin like you good folks is kind enough to think, a man of philosophy and easygoing nature. They was a thing happened when I was a young fella that set me on the right path, you might say. My father give me a flashlight for Christmas one year and the batteries wore out, like they is bound to do if a man aims to see more in this life than the good Lord wants him to. So I gave the flashlight to an uncle of mine, 'cause he sed he'd get it fixed for me. Well, he didn't *exactly* say he'd get it fixed for me. "I'm a-goin' by Burke's store," he sez, "where they has batteries. You want me to take it along?" So I sez that would be very kind of him. But he brung it back that evening and it wouldn't work when I clicked it. "Needs new batteries," sez my uncle, and when I told him he promised to have it fixed, he sez, "Never sed nuthin' 'bout havin' it fixed. Said I was goin' by Burke's store. Didn't say I was stoppin' in." Well, sir, like many a man, young or old, that ain't growed up – and some of 'em never does – I lost my temper. I seen red and I smashed that there flashlight into a thousand pieces. I realized in a second this wasn't no way to act to a man a greater age and more common sense'n me, so I turned it off with a joke. I turns to my uncle and I sez, solemn-like, "Defective," I sez. Then—'

I got up quietly and quickly from my chair and started to slip out of the chapel. A number of the men turned and stared at me, and several frowned and said, 'Sh!' Bill Logan plucked me by the sleeve as I passed his chair. 'Are you walking out on Zeph?' he whispered. I leaned down close to his ear. 'Yes,' I whispered. 'For ever.'

I had intended to spend the winter in Ludlow, but business took me back to the city, or, at least, I told Paul Morton and the others that business took me back to the city. My wife knew better, of course. She knew that Zeph Leggin was behind my determination to get out of Ludlow and stay out. Several months went by before I got up courage enough to tell her about the flashlight and Zeph Leggin's opening remarks on the night of the Forum meeting. To my surprise and delight, I discovered that I was able to laugh with her about what she called my straight-set defeat at the hands of the philosopher of Ludlow. She has promised, however, never to tell the Mortons about it, or Bill and Lucy Logan. I don't think I could stand that.

The Figgerin' of
Aunt Wilma

WHEN I was a boy, John Hance's grocery stood on the south side of Town Street, just east of Fourth, in the Central Market region of Columbus, Ohio. It was an old store even then, forty-five years ago, and its wide oak floor boards had been worn pleasantly smooth by the shoe soles of three generations of customers. The place smelt of coffee, peppermint, vinegar, and spices. Just inside the door on the left, a counter with a rounded glass front held all the old-fashioned penny candies – gumdrops, liquorice whips, horehound, and the rest – some of them a little pale with age. On the rear wall, between a barrel of dill pickles and a keg of salt mackerel in brine, there was an iron coffee grinder, whose handle I was sometimes allowed to turn.

Once, Mr Hance gave me a stick of Yucatan gum, an astonishing act of generosity, since he had a sharp sense of the value of a penny. Thrift was John Hance's religion. His store was run on a strictly cash basis. He shared the cost of his telephone with the Hays Carriage Shop next door. The instrument was set in a movable wooden cubicle that could be whirled through an opening in the west wall of the store. When I was ten, I used to hang around the grocery on Saturday afternoons, waiting for the telephone to disappear into the wall. Then I would wait for it to swing back again. It was a kind of magic, and I was disappointed to learn of its mundane purpose – the saving of a few dollars a month.

Mr Hance was nearly seventy, a short man with white hair and a white mustache and the most alert eyes that I can remember, except perhaps Aunt Wilma Hudson's. Aunt Wilma lived on South Sixth Street and always shopped at Mr Hance's store. Mr Hance's eyes were blue and capable of a keen concentration that could make you squirm. Aunt Wilma had black agate eyes that moved restlessly and scrutinized everybody with bright suspicion. In church, her glance would dart around the congregation seeking out irreverent men and women whose expressions showed that

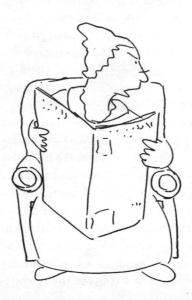

they were occupied with worldly concerns, or even carnal thoughts, in the holy place. If she lighted on a culprit, her heavy, dark brows would lower, and her mouth would tighten in righteous disapproval. Aunt Wilma was as honest as the day is long and as easily confused, when it came to what she called figgerin', as the night is dark. Her clashes with Mr Hance had become a family legend. He was a swift and competent calculator, and nearly fifty years of constant practice had enabled him to add up a column of figures almost at a glance. He set down his columns swiftly on an empty paper sack with a stubby black pencil. Aunt Wilma, on the other hand, was slow and painstaking when it came to figgerin'. She would go over and over a column of numbers, her glasses far down on her nose, her lips moving soundlessly. To her, rapid calculation, like all the other reckless and impulsive habits of men, was tainted with a kind of godlessness. Mr Hance always sighed when he looked up and saw her coming into his store. He knew that she could lift a simple dollar transaction into a dim and mystic realm of confusion all her own.

I was fortunate enough to be present one day in 1905 when Mr Hance's calculating and Aunt Wilma's figgerin' came together in memorable single combat. She had wheedled me into carrying her market basket, on the ground that it was going to be too heavy for her to manage. Her two grandsons, boys around my own age, had skipped out when I came to call at their house, and Aunt Wilma promptly seized on me. A young 'un, as she called everybody under seventeen, was not worth his salt if he couldn't help a body about the house. I had shopped with her before, under duress, and I knew her accustomed and invariable route on Saturday mornings, when Fourth Street, from Main to State, was lined with the stands of truck gardeners. Prices were incredibly low in those days, but Aunt Wilma questioned the cost, the quality, and the measure of everything. By the time she had finished her long and tedious purchases of fresh produce from the country, and we had turned east into Town Street and headed for Mr Hance's store, the weight of the market basket was beginning to pain my arm. 'Come along, child, come along,' Aunt Wilma snapped, her eyes shining with the look of the Middle Western housewife engaged in hard but virtuous battle with the wicked forces of the merchandising world.

I saw Mr Hance make a small involuntary gesture with his right hand as he spied Aunt Wilma coming through the door. He had just finished with a customer, and since his assistant was busy, he knew he was in for it. It took a good half-hour for Aunt Wilma to complete her shopping for groceries, but at length everything she wanted was stacked on the counter in sacks and cans and boxes. Mr Hance set deftly to work with his paper sack and pencil, jotting down the price of each article as he fitted it into the basket. Aunt Wilma watched his expert movements closely, like a hostile baseball fan waiting for an error in the infield. She regarded adroitness in a man as 'slick' rather than skillful.

Aunt Wilma's purchases amounted to ninety-eight cents. After writing down this sum, Mr Hance, knowing my aunt, whisked the paper bag around on the counter so that she could examine his addition. It took her some time, bending over and peering through her glasses, to arrive at a faintly reluctant corroboration of his figgerin'. Even when she was satisfied that all was in order, she had another go at the column of numbers, her lips moving silently as she added them up for the third time. Mr Hance waited patiently, the flat of his hands on the counter. He seemed to be fascinated by the movements of her lips. 'Well, I guess it's all right,' said Aunt Wilma, at last, 'but everything *is* so dear.' What she had bought for less than a dollar made the market basket bulge. Aunt Wilma took her purse out of her bag and drew out a dollar bill slowly and handed it over, as if it were a hundred dollars she would never see again.

Mr Hance deftly pushed the proper keys of the cash register, and the red hand on the indicator pointed to $.98. He studied the cash drawer, which had shot out at him. 'Well, well,' he said, and then, 'Hmm. Looks like I haven't got any pennies.' He turned back to Aunt Wilma. 'Have you got three cents, Mrs Hudson?' he asked.

That started it.

Aunt Wilma gave him a quick look of distrust. Her Sunday suspicion gleamed in her eyes. '*You owe me two cents*,' she said sharply.

'I know that, Mrs Hudson,' he sighed, 'but I'm out of pennies. Now, if you give me three cents, I'll give you a nickel.'

Aunt Wilma stared at him cautiously.

'It's all right if you give him three cents and he gives you a nickel,' I said.

'Hush up,' said Aunt Wilma. 'I'm figgerin'.' She figgered for several moments, her mouth working again.

Mr Hance slipped a nickel out of the drawer and placed in

on the counter. 'There is your nickel,' he said firmly. 'Now you just have to give me three cents.'

Aunt Wilma pecked about in her purse and located three pennies, which she brought out carefully, one at a time. She laid them on the counter beside the nickel, and Mr Hance reached for them. Aunt Wilma was too quick for him. She covered the eight cents with a lean hand. 'Wait, now!' she said, and she took her hand away slowly. She frowned over the four coins as if they were a difficult hand in bridge whist. She ran her lower lip against her upper teeth. 'Maybe if I give you a dime,' she said, 'and take the eight cents . . . It is *two* cents you're short, ain't it?'

Mr Hance began to show signs of agitation. One or two amused customers were now taking in the scene out of the corners of their eyes. 'No, no,' said Mr Hance. 'That way, you would be making me a present of seven cents!' This was too much for Aunt Wilma. She couldn't understand the new and preposterous sum of seven cents that had suddenly leaped at her from nowhere. The notion that she was about to do herself out of some money staggered her, and her eyes glazed for a moment like a groggy prizefighter's. Neither Mr Hance nor I said anything out of fear of deepening the tangle. She made an uncertain move of her right hand and I had the wild thought that she was going to give Mr Hance one of the pennies and scoop up the seven cents, but she didn't. She fell into a silent clinch with the situation and then her eyes cleared. 'Why, of *course*!' she cried brightly. 'I don't know what got into me! You take the eight cents and give me a dime. Then I'll have the two cents that's coming to me.' One of the customers laughed, and Aunt Wilma cut

him down with a swift glare. The diversion gave me time to
figure out that whereas Mr Hance had been about to gain
seven cents, he was now going to lose a nickel. 'That way, *I*
would be making *you* a present of *five* cents, Mrs Hudson,'
he said stiffly. They stood motionless for several seconds,
each trying to stare the other down.

'Now, here,' said Mr Hance, turning and taking her dollar
out of the still open cash drawer. He laid it beside the nickel
and the pennies. 'Now, here,' he said again. 'You gave me a
dollar three, but you don't own me a dollar three – you own
me five cents less than that. Here is the five cents.' He
snatched it up and handed it to her. She held the nickel
between thumb and forefinger, and her eyes gleamed briefly,
as if she at last comprehended the peculiar deal, but the
gleam faded. Suddenly she handed him his nickel and picked
up her dollar and her three cents. She put the pennies back
in her purse. 'I've rung up the ninety-eight cents, Mrs
Hudson,' said Mr Hance quickly. 'I must have the dollar
back in the till.' He turned and pointed at the $.98 on the
indicator. 'I tell you what. If you'll give me the dollar, I'll
give you the nickel, and we'll call it square.' She obviously
didn't want to take the nickel or give up the dollar, but she
did, finally. I was astounded at first, for here was the
penny-careful Mr Hance knocking three cents off a bill, but
then I realized he was afraid of losing the dollar and was
willing to settle for the lesser of two evils.

'Well,' said Aunt Wilma irritably, 'I'm sure I don't know
what you're trying to do.' I was a timid boy, but I had to
plunge into the snarl, if only on behalf of the family honor.
'Gee, Aunt Wilma,' I told her, 'if you keep the nickel, he's

giving you everything for ninety-five cents.'

Mr Hance scowled hard at me. He was afraid I was going to get him in deeper than he already was. 'It's all right, son,' he said. 'It's all right.' He put the dollar in the till and shoved the drawer shut with a decisive bang, but I wasn't going to give up.

'Gee, whizz, Aunt Wilma,' I complained, 'you still owe him three cents. Don't you see that?'

She gave me the pitying glance of a superior and tired intelligence. 'I never owed him three cents in my life,' she said tartly. 'He owes me two cents. You stay out of things you don't understand.'

'It's all right,' said Mr Hance again, in a weary voice. He was sure that if she scrabbled in her purse again for the three pennies, she would want her dollar back, and they would be right where they had started. I gave my aunt a look of disenchantment.

'Now, wait!' she cried suddenly. 'Maybe I have the exact change! I don't know what's got into me I didn't think of that! I think I have the right change after all.' She put back on the counter the nickel she had been clutching in her left hand, and then she began to peck at the coins in her purse and, after a good minute, arranged two quarters, four dimes, Mr Hance's nickel, and three pennies on the counter. 'There,' she said, her eyes flashing triumph. 'Now you give me my dollar back.'

Mr Hance sighed deeply, rang out the cash drawer by pushing 'No Sale,' and handed her the dollar. Then he hastily scraped up the change, deposited each coin in its proper place in the till, and slammed the drawer shut again.

I was only ten, and mathematics was not my best study, but it wasn't hard to figure that Mr Hance, who in the previous arrangement had been out three cents, was now out five cents. 'Good day, Mrs Hudson,' he said grimly. He felt my sympathetic eyes on him, and we exchanged a brief, knowing masculine glance of private understanding.

'Good day, Mr Hance,' said Aunt Wilma, and her tone was as grim as the grocer's.

I took the basket from the counter, and Mr Hance sighed again, this time with relief. 'Goodbye, goodbye,' he said with false heartiness, glad to see us on our way. I felt I should slip him the parsley, or whatever sack in the basket had cost a nickel.

'Come on, child,' said Aunt Wilma. 'It's dreadfully late. I declare it's taken hours to shop today.' She muttered plaintively all the way out of the store.

I noticed as I closed the door behind us that Mr Hance was waiting on a man customer. The man was laughing. Mr Hance frowned and shrugged.

As we walked east on Town Street, Aunt Wilma let herself go. 'I never heard of such a thing in all the born days of my life,' she said. 'I don't know where John Hance got his schooling, if he got any. The very idea – a grown man like that getting so mixed up. Why, I could have spent the whole day in that store and he'd never of figgered it out. Let him keep the two cents, then. It was worth it to get out of that store.'

'*What* two cents, Aunt Wilma?' I almost squealed.

'Why the two cents he still owes me!' she said. 'I don't know what they teach you young 'uns nowadays. Of course he owes me two cents. It come to ninety-eight cents and I give him a dollar. He owed me two cents in the beginning and he still owes me two cents. Your Uncle Herbert will explain it to you. Any man in the world could figger it out except John Hance.'

I walked on beside her in silence, thinking of Uncle Herbert, a balding, choleric man of high impatience and quick temper.

'Now, you let *me* explain it to your Uncle Herbert, child,' she said. 'I declare you were as mixed up as John Hance was. If I'd of listened to you and given him the three cents, like you said, I'd never of got my dollar back. He'd owe me five cents instead of two. Why, it's as plain as day.'

I thought I had the solution for her now, and I leaped at it. 'That's right, Aunt Wilma,' I almost yelled. 'He owed you a nickel and he gave you the nickel.'

Aunt Wilma stabbed me with her indignation. 'I gave *him* the nickel,' she said. 'I put it on the counter right there under your very eyes, and you saw him scoop it up.'

I shifted the market basket to my left arm. 'I know, Aunt Wilma,' I said, 'but it was *his* nickel all the time.'

She snorted, 'Well, he'd got his precious nickel, ain't he?' she demanded. I shifted the basket back again. I thought I detected a faint trace of uneasiness in her tone. She fell silent and quickened her cadence, and it was hard for me to keep up with her. As we turned south into Sixth Street, I glanced up and saw that she was frowning and that her lips were moving again. She was rehearsing the story of the strange transaction for Uncle Herbert. I began to whistle. 'Hush up, child,' she said, 'I'm figgerin'.'

*

Uncle Herbert was sitting in the living-room, eating an apple. I could tell from his expression that he was in one of his rare amiable moods. Aunt Wilma grabbed the basket away from me. 'Now, you let me explain it to your uncle,' she said. 'You wait till I get back.' She sailed out of the room on her way to the kitchen.

A little breathlessly, I told Uncle Herbert the saga of Aunt Wilma's complicated financial quandary. He was chuckling when she came back into the room.

Uncle Herbert's amusement nettled her. 'The boy got it wrong,' she said accusingly. 'He didn't tell it right. He was ever' bit as mixed up as John Hance.' Uncle Herbert's chuckle increased to full and open laughter. Aunt Wilma glared at him until he subsided. 'Now, Herbert, you listen to me,' she began, but he cut in on her.

'If Hance ever gives you that two cents he owes you, Wilma,' he said, 'I tell you what you have to do to square accounts. Someday you're going to have to give him a dime for three cents.' He began to laugh again.

Aunt Wilma Hudson stared at each of us in turn, with a look of fine, cold scorn, and then she raised both her hands and let them fall helplessly. 'I declare,' she said, 'I don't know how the world gets along with the men runnin' it.'

My Own Ten Rules for a Happy Marriage

NOBODY, I hasten to announce, has asked me to formulate a set of rules for the perpetuation of marital bliss and the preservation of the tranquil American boudoir and inglenook. The idea just came to me one day, when I watched a couple in an apartment across the court from mine gesturing and

banging tables and throwing *objets d'art* at each other. I couldn't hear what they were saying, but it was obvious, as the shot-put followed the hammer throw, that he and/or she (as the lawyers would put it) had deeply offended her and/or him.

Their apartment, before they began to take it apart, had been quietly and tastefully arranged, but it was a little hard to believe this now, as he stood there by the fireplace, using an andiron to bat back the Royal Doulton figurines she was curving at him from her strongly entrenched position behind the davenport. I wondered what had started the exciting but costly battle, and, brooding on the general subject of Husbands and Wives, I found myself compiling my own Ten Rules for a Happy Marriage.

I have avoided the timeworn admonitions, such as 'Praise her new hat,' 'Share his hobbies,' 'Be a sweetheart as well as a wife,' and 'Don't keep a blonde in the guest room,' not only because they are threadbare from repetition, but also because they don't seem to have accomplished their purpose. Maybe what we need is a brand-new set of rules. Anyway, ready or not, here they come, the result of fifty years (I began as a little boy) spent in studying the nature and behavior, mistakes and misunderstandings, of the American Male (*homo Americansis*) and his Mate.

RULE ONE: Neither party to a sacred union should run down, disparage or badmouth the other's former girls or beaux, as the case may be. The tendency to attack the character, looks, intelligence, capability, and achievements of one's mate's former friends of the opposite sex is a common cause of domestic discontent. Sweetheart-slurring, as we will call this deplorable practice, is encouraged by a long spell of gloomy weather, too many highballs, hang-overs, and the suspicion that one's spouse is hiding, and finding, letters in a hollow tree, or is intercepting the postman, or putting in secret phone calls from the corner drugstore. These fears almost always turn out to be unfounded, but the unfounded fear, as we all know, is worse than the founded.

Aspersions, insinuations, reflections or just plain cracks about old boy friends and girl friends should be avoided at all times. Here are some of the expressions that should be especially eschewed: 'That waffle-fingered, minor-league third baseman you latched on to at Cornell'; 'You know the girl I mean – the one with the hips who couldn't read'; 'That old flame of yours with the vocabulary of a hoot owl'; and 'You remember her – that old bat who chewed gum and dressed like Daniel Boone.'

This kind of derogatory remark, if persisted in by one or both parties to a marriage, will surely lead to divorce or, at best, a blow on the head with a glass ash tray.

RULE TWO: A man should make an honest effort to get the names of his wife's friends right. This is not easy. The average wife who has graduated from college at any time during the past thirty years keeps in close touch with at least seven old classmates. These ladies, known as 'the girls,' are named, respectively: Mary, Marian, Melissa, Marjorie, Maribel, Madeleine, and Miriam; and all of them are called Myrtle by the careless husband we are talking about. Furthermore, he gets their nicknames wrong. This, to be sure, is understandable, since their nicknames are, respectively: Molly, Muffy, Missy, Midge, Mabby, Maddy, and Mims. The careless husband, out of thoughtlessness or pure cussedness, calls them all Mugs, or, when he is feeling particularly brutal, Mucky.

All the girls are married, one of them to a Ben Tompkins, and as this is the only one he can remember, our hero calls all the husbands Ben, or Tompkins, adding to the general annoyance and confusion.

If you are married to a college graduate, then, try to get the names of her girl friends and their husbands straight. This will prevent some of those interminable arguments that begin after Midge and Harry (not Mucky and Ben) have said a stiff goodnight and gone home.

RULE THREE: A husband should not insult his wife publicly, at parties. He should insult her in the privacy of the home. Thus, if a man thinks the soufflés his wife makes are as tough as an outfielder's glove, he should tell her so when they are at home, not when they are out at a formal dinner party, where a perfect soufflé has just been served. The same rule applies to the wife. She should not regale his men friends, or women friends, with hilarious accounts of her husband's clumsiness, remarking that he dances like a 1907 Pope Hartford, or that he locked himself in the children's rabbit pen and couldn't get out. All parties must end finally, and the husband or wife who has revealed all may find there is hell to pay in the taxi going home.

RULE FOUR: The wife who keeps saying, 'Isn't that just like a man?' and the husband who keeps saying, 'Oh, well, you know how women are,' are likely to grow farther and farther apart through the years. These famous generalizations have the effect of reducing an individual to the anonymous status of a mere unit in a mass. The wife who, just in time, comes upon her husband about to fry an egg in a dry skillet should not classify him with all other males but should give him the accolade of a special distinction. She might say, for example, 'George, no other man in the world would try to do a thing like that.' Similarly, a husband watching his wife laboring to start the car without turning on the ignition should not say to the gardener or a passer-by, 'Oh, well, you know, etc.' Instead, he should remark to his wife, 'I've seen a lot of women in my life, Nellie, but I've never seen one who could touch you.'

Certain critics of this rule will point out that the specific comments I would substitute for the old familiar generalizations do not solve the problem. They will maintain that the husband and wife will be sore and sulky for several days, no matter what is said. One wife, reading Rule Four over my shoulder, exclaimed, 'Isn't that just like a man?' This brings us right back where we started. Oh, well, you know how women are!

RULE FIVE: When a husband is reading aloud, a wife should sit quietly in her chair, relaxed but attentive. If he has decided to read the Republican platform, an article on elm blight, or a blow-by-blow account of a prize fight, it is not going to be easy, but she should at least pretend to be interested. She should not keep swinging one foot, start to wind her wrist watch, file her fingernails, or clap her hands in an effort to catch a mosquito. The good wife allows the mosquito to bite her when her husband is reading aloud.

She should not break in to correct her husband's pronunciation, or to tell him one of his socks is wrong side out. When the husband has finished, the wife should not lunge instantly into some irrelevant subject. It's wiser to exclaim: 'How interesting!' or, at the very least, 'Well, well!' She might even compliment him on his diction and his grasp of politics, elm blight or boxing. If he should ask some shrewd question to test her attention, she can cry, 'Good heavens!' leap up, and rush out to the kitchen on some urgent fictitious errand. This may fool him, or it may not. I hope, for her sake – and his – that it does.

RULE SIX: A husband should try to remember where things are around the house so that he does not have to wait for his wife to get home from the hairdresser's before he can put his hands on what he wants. Among the things a husband is usually unable to locate are the iodine, the aspirin, the nail file, the French vermouth, his cuff links, studs, black silk socks and evening shirts, the snapshots taken at Nantucket last summer, his favorite record of 'Kentucky Babe,' the borrowed copy of *The Road to Miltown*, the garage key, his own towel, the last bill from Brooks Brothers, his pipe cleaners, the poker chips, crackers, cheese, the whetstone, his new raincoat, and the screens for the upstairs windows.

MY OWN TEN RULES

I don't really know the solution to this problem, but one should be found. Perhaps every wife should draw for her husband a detailed map of the house, showing clearly the location of everything he might need. Trouble is, I suppose, he would lay the map down somewhere and not be able to find it until his wife got home.

RULE SEVEN: If a husband is not listening to what his wife is saying, he should not grunt, 'Okay' or 'Yeah, sure,' or make little affirmative noises. A husband lost in thought or worry is likely not to take in the sense of such a statement as this: 'We're going to the Gordons for dinner tonight, John, so I'm letting the servants off. Don't come home from the office first. Remember, we both have to be at the dentist's at five, and I'll pick you up there with the car.' Now, an 'Okay,' or a 'Yeah, sure' at this point can raise havoc if the husband hasn't really been listening. As usual, he goes all the way out to his home in Glenville – thirteen miles from the dentist's office and seventeen miles from the Gordons' house – and he can't find his wife. He can't find the servants. His wife can't get him on the phone because all she gets is the busy buzz. John is calling everybody he can think of except, of course, the dentist and the Gordons. At last he hangs up, exhausted and enraged. Then the phone rings. It is his wife. And here let us leave them.

RULE EIGHT: If your husband ceases to call you 'Sugarfoot' or 'Candy Eyes' or 'Cutie Fudge Pie' during the first year of your marriage, it is not necessarily a sign that he has come to take you for granted or that he no longer cares. It is probably an indication that he has recovered his normal perspective. Many a young husband who once call his wife 'Tender Mittens' or 'Taffy Ears' or 'Rose Lips' has become austere or important, like a common pleas Judge, and he wouldn't want reports of his youthful frivolity to get around. If he doesn't call you Dagmar when your name is Daisy, you are sitting pretty.

RULE NINE: For those whose husbands insist on pitching for the Married Men against the Single Men at the Fourth-of-July picnic of the First M. E. Church, I have the following suggestion; don't sit on the sidelines and watch him. Get lost. George is sure to be struck out by a fourteen-year-old boy, pull up with a charley horse running to first, and get his teeth knocked out by an easy grounder to the mound. When you see him after the game, tell him everybody knew the little boy was throwing illegal spitballs, everybody saw the first baseman spike George, and everybody said that grounder took such a nasty bounce even Phil Rizzuto couldn't have fielded it. Remember, most middle-aged husbands get to sleep at night by imagining they are striking out the entire batting order of the Yankees.

RULE TEN: A wife's dressing table should be inviolable. It is the one place in the house a husband should get away from and stay away from. And yet, the average husband is drawn to it as by a magnet, especially when he is carrying something wet, oily, greasy or sticky, such as a universal joint, a hub cap, or the blades of a lawn mower. His excuse for bringing these alien objects into his wife's bedroom in the first place is that he is looking for 'an old rag' with which to wipe them off. There are no old rags in a lady's boudoir, but husbands never seem to learn this. They search hampers, closets, and bureau drawers, expecting to find a suitable piece of cloth, but first they set the greasy object on the dressing table. The aggrieved wife may be tempted, following this kind of vandalism, to lock her bedroom door and kick her husband out for good. I suggest, however, a less stringent punishment. Put a turtle in his bed. The wife who is afraid to pick up a turtle should ask Junior to help her. Junior will love it.

Now I realize, in glancing back over these rules, that some of my solutions to marital problems may seem a little untidy; that I have, indeed, left a number of loose ends here and there. For example, if the husbands are going to mislay their detailed maps of household objects, I have accomplished nothing except to add one item for the distraught gentleman to lose.

Then, there is that turtle. Captious critics will point out that a turtle in a husband's bed is not a valid solution to anything, but merely a further provocation. The outraged husband will deliberately trip his wife during their next mixed-doubles match. She will thereupon retaliate but putting salt in his breakfast coffee. . . .

Two persons living in holy matrimony, I should have said long before this, must avoid slipping into blasphemy, despond, apathy, and the subjunctive mood. A husband is always set on edge by his mate's 'Far be it from me' or 'Be that as it may.' This can lead to other ominous openings: 'Would God that' and 'Had I only had the good sense to,' and the couple is then in the gloomy sub-cellar of the pluperfect subjunctive, a place in which no marriage can thrive. The safest place for a happily wedded pair is the indicative mood, and of its tenses the present is the most secure. The future is a domain of threats and worries, and the past is a wasteland of sorrows and regrets.

I can only hope, in conclusion, that this treatise itself will not start, in any household, a widening gap that can never be closed.

The Pleasure Cruise,
and How to Survive It

IT HAS occurred to me that there may be persons here and
there, young and inexperienced in the ways of the world,
who might profit from my own personal TRAVEL HINTS,
compiled after looking back on thirty-odd years of knocking
about, or being knocked about, the globe. I don't mean the
whole globe, of course. I have never been south of Trinidad,
north of Quebec, east of Italy, or west of San Francisco, but
within these rather roomy limits, I have been knocked about
quite a bit.

My first hint – to the gentleman traveler – is a simple
one. Never go anywhere without your wife. If your wife
won't go, because the concert or canning season is on, or
something of the sort, take your sister or your mother or
your cousin. The American woman is indispensable in getting
the tickets and reservations, packing and unpacking, mixing
Bromo-Seltzers, fending off beautiful ladies who are traveling
alone, and making herself useful generally. Hers is also the
only sex that can successfully close a wardrobe trunk. If a
man closes a wardrobe trunk, there is always a sharp snapping
sound, caused by the breaking of something that will not
bend, such as the handle of a mirror, or the stem of a
Dunhill pipe, or the stopper of a perfume bottle. If a woman

is deprived of her Chanel No. 5 during, say, a nineteen-day cruise, she will become irritable, and there is nothing more exasperating on a cruise, or anywhere else, than an irritable female companion.

Now that I have mentioned cruises, let us consider more closely the technique of the sea voyage. After the wife has closed the wardrobe trunk and called a taxi, it is only eight in the morning, and the ship doesn't sail till eleven. The husband will complain that it doesn't take three hours to get to a pier only eight blocks from their hotel. He will point out that they can get to Pier 58 in half an hour, with time to spare. He is right, it turns out, but it also turns out that he doesn't know where Pier 58 is. His wife has unfortunately left this one small detail up to him. He tells the taxi driver to take them to the foot of West 58th Street, but when they get there, it transpires that this is not the point of departure of their ship, the *Santa Maria*. It is the point of departure of the *J. B. Cathcart*, a coastwise fruit steamer bound for French Guiana. The taxi driver suggests that the *Santa Maria* probably sails from Brooklyn or Hoboken. The husband figures there is time to try both places, but his wife's sounder judgment prevails. She asks somebody – always an excellent idea – where Pier 58 is, and is told Pier 58 is at the foot of West 16th Street. It is too.

On the way to the right destination, with time to spare – just as the husband had promised – the taxi driver suddenly has a hunch that the *Santa Maria* sails at 11 p.m., on Tuesdays, and not at 11 a.m., on Thursdays. This throws his male passenger into a panic. The seasoned woman traveler pays no attention to all this unnecessary masculine excitement.

She leans back in the cab, closes her eyes and wonders if she forgot to pack her white piqué evening dress. Once aboard the ship, the wife (Ellen) tells her husband (George) that she has to unpack her light things right away or they will crush, and she asks him, for heaven's sake, to get deck chairs on the sunny and windless side of the ship immediately, before they are all gone, and also to make table reservations instantly, so they can have a table for two once in their lives, and not have to sit with a lot of strangers. George wanders away on these important errands and (1) runs into an old classmate from Dartmouth and (2) decides that they ought to find out where the bar is and what time it opens for business. When he returns to his stateroom, an hour later, Ellen is in excellent spirits – she has found the white piqué evening dress – but her amiable mood is not going to last very long. 'Did you reserve the chairs and the table?' she asked. 'Hm?' says George blankly. I will spare you the scene that follows. Suffice to say that the Kendalls (their name is Kendall) have to settle for deck chairs on the sunless and windy side of the ship, and are put at a table for eight: two women buyers from Cleveland, an embalmer and his bride, a pair of giggling college girls and Mr and Mrs George Kendall. She has the chair with the short right-rear leg.

My private tip here is that the wife should reserve the deck chairs and the table, let the dresses crush where they may, but I have never been able to sell the idea to any woman traveler.

The only woman who doesn't care whether her dresses crush or not is the seasick woman, but I wouldn't recommend seasickness as the way out of anything, not even the way out of sitting next to the embalmer at dinner. Speaking of seasickness, I am unlucky enough to have a stomach of platinum, and I haven't suffered from *mal de mer* since the eastward Atlantic crossing of the USS *Orizaba*, in November, 1918, but this was a transport that took nine days zig-zagging from New York to St Nazaire in heavy weather, and there was an honorable excuse for my condition. I say I am 'unlucky' enough to have a stomach of platinum, because the seasick turn to the unseasick on a ship for succor, sanctuary and salvation that are impossible to give. Once, on the Bermuda run – seventeen of us up and around on the second day, out of a passenger list of three hundred – I came upon a lone woman sprawled on a sofa in the library up forward, where rolling and pitching had flung her prostrate and forlorn. She lay on her hat and her right side; one shoe was off; her handbag was open on the floor, its contents scattered; her lipstick was smudged in such a way that she seemed to have bitten her own left cheek. I was appalled – sympathetic, gallant even, but appalled – and when I am appalled, my nervous system becomes an apparatus that, as the French would say, *ne fonctionne pas*.

'Do something,' she said in a faint, awful voice.

'Madam,' I squeaked helplessly. I was unable to say anything, but I did something. I put her things back in her handbag and placed it on a table.

'I put your handbag on the table,' I finally managed to croak.

'Do something,' she said again, in the same voice. For a moment I considered putting her shoe back on, but like any other Ohio State man, I was restrained by the feeling that the act would be both insensitive and foolish. Then I suddenly decided to put the shoe on the table with the handbag.

'Do something,' she said, in a weaker tone. I staggered out of the library, hunted up a deck steward and told him about the lady and her extremity.

'Do something,' I begged him. He just shook his head sadly. I rolled on my way, and came to an elevator that ran from A Deck down to E Deck and back. There was a woman there, frantically pressing the bell button. She was standing, she had both shoes on, but she looked just as ghastly as the lost lady in the library. She grabbed my arm as I tried to walk by.

'E Deck. Quick!' she gasped.

'The elevator will be up—' I began and caught myself, but not in time. Her face took on a saffron hue.

'I'm sorry,' I mumbled. She looked at me with the eyes of a stepped-on spaniel.

'E Deck,' she said again. 'Please.'

I had to do something. I brushed past her and began pushing the bell button wildly. Then I turned and ran. I have often wondered, in my own low and agonized moments, if she made it.

Just what hint to give to the unseasick passenger who may be faced, during an ocean voyage, with crises and suffering similar to my own that terrible day, I frankly do not know. There are certain tortures that we unseasick passengers simply have to endure, I guess. I would appreciate it, though, if you don't go around saying that, in the emergencies I have described, I just 'got the hell out.' I did what I could. There will, of course, always be two schools of thought about that shoe, the school that contends I should have put it back on, and the school that insists I should have let it lie where I found it. Apparently nobody in the world but me would have put it on the table with the handbag. I can only say that if I had it all to do over again, I would still put the shoe on the table with the handbag.

If you travel much on ships you are bound, sooner or later, to run into Mrs Abigail Pritchard, as I shall call her. She is not just one woman, but many; I have encountered at least fifteen of her. Mrs Pritchard may be forty-five, or she may be seventy, but her average age, I should say, is about fifty-seven. She comes from Boston, Hartford, Germantown, Syracuse, Toledo, Chicago, Louisville, St Louis, Denver, Sacramento, and both Portlands. She is a widow, fairly well off, whose children are happily married and the fathers, or mothers, of the prettiest and brightest youngsters in the world, and she has snapshots and anecdotes to prove it. She takes two Daiquiris before dinner and a highball after-wards, and smokes Players, on the ground that they are made of actual tobacco, whereas American cigarettes, in her opinion, are composed of rum, molasses, shredded cork, and factory sweepings. She prefers domestic Burgundies, how-ever, because the so-called French vintages you find on ships are really only cheap Algerian wine that has been poured into genuine bottles labeled Pommard or Chablis. Mrs Pritchard is full of interesting little anecdotes about the late Sir Harry Oakes, the late Richard Halliburton ('that dear boy'), a Colonel Grosvenor in Penang, the gifted Courtney girls (whoever they are), John Barrymore ('poor old Jack'), Heifetz, Houdini, Nell Brinkley, Anna Eva Fay, Percy Marmont, Maurice Costello ('the king of them all'), Kip Rhinelander, Mrs O. H. P. Belmont, Struthers Burt, Ky Laffoon and anybody else whose name you happen to mention. Mrs Pritchard is certain she saw Judge Crater in the Casino at Cannes in 1937, where he was known as Maltby or Goadby, or some such. 'How do you do, Judge Crater?' she said to him firmly. He started – there could be no doubt of that. 'My name is Maltby (or Goadby), madam,' the man said, and hurried away.

Mrs Pritchard can invariably spot, aboard ship, professional gamblers, unmarried couples sharing the same stateroom, fugitives from justice, fingermen formerly in the employ of Al Capone, cocaine sniffers, bay-rum drinkers, professional men of dubious integrity, women who are mortally ill but don't know it, unhappy wives and gentlemen with phony foreign accents. It makes you nervous to talk to, or rather listen to, Mrs Pritchard. You twist restlessly in your chair, confident that she has figured you for an absconder, a black-marketeer, or a white-slave trader. Mrs Pritchard spends at least two months of every year on ships, but I often wonder why, since she suspects that there is skulduggery afoot from the chart room to the hold. If the ship is even half an hour late in shoving off, she whispers that 'Uncle Joe is behind this delay.' She never clears this up, though, but merely shakes her head wisely, if you ask her what she means. She is sure the ship is going to put to sea with broken pumps, insufficient lifeboats, and a typhoid carrier among the crew. Two days out, she tells you she doesn't like the look of the saxophone player's complexion

– he has something contagious, mark her words. The third day out she declares that the chief steward is secreting fifteen thousand pounds of roast beef, which he intends to sell to a syndicate in Port-au-Prince. It costs ten thousand dollars a day to operate a ship, she read in the *Reader's Digest*, and this ridiculous amount is due to thefts of supplies by the stewards.

Even the captain of the ship is not above her suspicion. She is positive that he forgot to order all those automobiles in the hold lashed down, and she knows they will roll to one side if a storm comes up, causing the ship to list, like the *Vestris*, and sink. Mrs Pritchard loves to tell about the time the master of an ocean liner was seized with a heart attack while steering the boat – she still thinks he was an epileptic – and almost ran into an iceberg. But her favorite story is about the time she was on a West Indies cruise, and caught a glimpse of the captain one day. She recognized him instantly as Major Quantrell (or Chantress, or some such name) wanted in Rangoon for the shooting of a missionary's daughter in a fashionable gambling house. Mrs Pritchard points out that a captain's cabin is the perfect hide-out for fugitives from justice, since nobody is allowed in the cabin except the officers, and they are probably no better than they ought to be, themselves.

The young traveler will naturally expect, old, experienced me to advise him how to avoid, or to deal with, Mrs Pritchard. Well, you can't avoid her. Just dismiss that from your mind. She pops up from everywhere and out from behind everything. Even if you hid in the engine room, she would search you out. As for dealing with the old girl, I have invented a rather nasty game called Back Her in the Corner, which works wonders.

'You know the Hotel l'Aiglon in Roquebrune, of course?' I say to her, casually.

'To be sure,' she replies. 'That perfectly gorgeous view of the Bay of Monte Carlo at night!'

We both look dreamy.

'Ah, yes,' I sigh, 'and those wonderful sardines grilled in triple-sec!'

'Yes, yes,' she sighs, 'those delicious sardines.'

You see, she has to keep up a show of having been every place I have been. And here's where my game gets nasty.

'There isn't any Hotel l'Aiglon in Roquebrune,' I say coldly, 'and there aren't any sardines grilled in triple-sec.'

She is furious. I have tricked her, and hell hath no fury like a woman tricked. She gives me a wide berth after that, not even nodding or smiling when I pass her on deck. I can get away with this little game because I am fifty-six,* but such conduct on the part of the *young* traveler would seem imprudent, disrespectful and ill-bred. You'll have to devise your own method of dealing with Mrs Pritchard. You mustn't expect me to solve *all* your travel problems. And please don't write to me and ask me what to do in the event that you run into the gifted Courtney sisters. I simply do not know.

A few days out of New York (if you sailed from New York), printed copies of the passenger list are usually distributed, containing such names as Jowes, Qmith, Johnsob, Crazier,

---

* Publisher's note: He's fifty-eight if he's a day.

Aprker, Sommonx and Spider. It takes years of practice to decipher some passenger-list garbles. The letters of my own name have assumed some twenty different permutations, but I am most often listed simply as Jane Phurber, a winsome six-foot Ohio matron who affects men's clothes. My wife, whose name is Helen Thurber, turned up on one ship under the alias of H. Muriel. In some mysterious manner, our false names (I was Joseph Thacher on this occasion) followed us ashore when we debarked at Naples. My wife indignantly showed our true passport names to one Italian official who had insisted we were one J. Thacher and one H. Muriel. He saw his mistake.

'I am all of regret, *signorina*,' he said, in excellent English, 'and expressing sorrows towards you and Signor Muriel.'

'Come on, H.,' I said, 'let's go.'

'OK, Joe,' she said, and we got out of there.

You will most likely have been at sea a week before you get around to reading the literature you picked up at your travel agency, or at the offices of the steamship line itself. This company gets out a pamphlet entitled *General Information*, and you should have read it before you got on the ship. It lists a number of things that should not be carried in a passenger's luggage: 'Dangerous articles, such as fireworks, matches, gunpowder, inflammable liquids, cartridges, inflammable motion-picture films.' If you have a supply of skyrockets and Roman candles, it would be wise to dump them overboard some night when nobody is watching you. Skyrockets shot from decks accidentally or out of a misguided burst of patriotic spirit are certain to be construed as signals of distress by other vessels, and this would vex the commander of your ship, to say the least. So leave your fireworks at home, in a safe, locked place, where the children can't get at them. I don't know why you keep fireworks in your house, anyway, but, of course, that is none of my business.

If you have gone on a cruise to relax, and you don't want to romp, run, race or wrestle, stay away from the sports director, a big, energetic blond young man carrying a medicine ball. The female of this species, the sports directress, is active, alert, athletic, aggressive and capable of throwing your wife, or you, over her shoulder with her left hand. If you are not in training and under twenty-eight, don't monkey around with these two. They will run you ragged. They love squatting exercises, chinning themselves, holding their breath, standing on their hands, and touching the deck two thousand times with their finger tips, without bending their knees. Don't try to keep up with them. Refuse their challenges, ignore their taunts. You can't beat them at anything from squatting to ping-pong, unless you are young Mathias, the decathlon champion, and you probably aren't. The sports directors are supposed to organize group recreational activities. This is both a fact and a warning.

Speaking of ping-pong, I once entered a table-tennis tournament aboard the SS *President Garfield*, on a trip from New York through the Canal to Los Angeles. The sports director was determined to get me into the table-tennis tournament, probably because he wanted to see me humiliated in the finals. And he did. I lost two straight games to a pretty, attractive young lady, twenty years* my

* Publisher's note: Twenty-two years.

junior. The table was too short, the net was too high, the rackets were warped, the ship rocked, a small boy among the spectators began riding me and I got something in my eye. I explained to my opponent after the match that, on land and under fair and reasonable conditions, I could have pinned her ears back, the best day she ever saw. She was honest enough to admit this. A very pleasant girl, and the luckiest woman I have ever met on sea or land.

The night before a ship makes home port at the end of a cruise, there is usually a ship's concert, or program of entertainment, in which the Courtney sisters and other gifted passengers are invited to take part. If you are a singer, violinist, bird caller, soft-shoe dancer, whistler, mimic, monologist, contortionist, juggler, hypnotist, ventriloquist, swami, *diseuse* or zither player, you are likely to be asked to join in the fun and do your act. You may refuse, of course, and you should, if you plan to recite all of *Evangeline* or *Hiawatha*. Your fellow-passengers will resent any act that lasts longer than five minutes. Once, coming back from the West Indies on the *Conte Grande*, I declined to appear on the concert program, and then suddenly, during a lull at midnight, I grabbed up a lighted megaphone and sang 'Who?' and 'Bye Bye Blackbird' with the orchestra. Well, not *with* it, exactly, since in 'Blackbird', I was singing '*Oh, the hard-luck stories they all hand me*' while the orchestra was playing '*No one here can love or understand me,*' but we were tied at the finish, I am happy to say. The survivors of that concert will doubtless remember my act, but they will not care to dwell on it any more than I do.

Since my performance that midnight, and possibly because of it, some of the more cautious cruise ships have eliminated passenger participation and turned the program of the final night over to professionals. The last cruise I was on, a few months ago, had no place for amateurs on the Big Night. The entertainment department of WOR provided a soprano, a baritone (to replace me), a prestidigitator, a couple of 'dance stylists,' an accordionist and several other instrumentalists. Talented passengers who had counted on imitating Tallulah Bankhead or playing 'Canadian Capers' on a makeshift xylophone composed of White Rock bottles were somewhat mollified when they were given funny hats to wear, horns to blow, bells to ring, and rattles to rattle at the Gala Farewell Dinner that preceded the Gala Farewell Revue. In charge of these Galas, and such affairs as the Fancy Headdress Ball and other intellectual goings on, are the cruise director and the cruise directress (not to be confused with the sports director and the sports directress). When, on my recent cruise, I returned to my stateroom after the Gala Farewell Revue, I found a cheerful note from the cruise director. It read: 'Rise up in the morning with the will that – smooth or rough – you'll grin!' I decided against this. You never know how a customs man may interpret a grin, especially a fixed grin.

Customs inspection is seldom as trying as you think it's going to be, unless you have a shoeful of diamonds or a trunk full of liqueurs. Just take your place under your proper letter (Q for Smith, E for Perkins, P for Thurber, and so forth) and see that you have assembled all your baggage. You will usually find that your typewriter case is missing and that you

have a large grey suitcase that doesn't belong to you. The person who owns the grey suitcase may have your type-writer, and he may not. Don't get excited and rush around accusing people of stealing your Corona, just relax. You have all day, you know, and if you went to bed instead of to the bar after the Gala Revue, you will find yourself taking this ancient formality in your stride. It is important not to get mad at your inspector because he wants to go through your effects. This is his job. A Virginian I know, a man impatient of red tape and fiddle-faddle, as he describes all activities of the United States Government, once addressed a group of three customs inspectors as follows: 'Gentlemen, you are clearly insane.' He was the last man off the dock that day.

No travel hints would be complete without some word of caution about shipboard romances, engagements and marriages. The girl or young man you fell in love with on the ship when it was in Southern waters and the orchestra was playing 'Night and Day' is going to be subjected to a cruel and rigorous test standing there by the gloomy pile of baggage in a bleak and chilly ship shed. If the swan suddenly becomes a goose, or the knight a clodhopper, it is what is known as 'undergoing a land change.' If you were married aboard ship and the bride, or bridegroom, now appeals to you about as much as a piece of cold whole-wheat toast, you are in a rather serious jam. In America you cannot have a marriage annulled on the ground that it was contracted while you were under the influence of the Gulf Stream or Cole Porter. If you are a man, I suggest that you treat your inamorata with a gallantry tempered by caution during the voyage out and back, and refrain from proposing until you have caught her on the dock. If she is going to be met by her mother and father, her Aunt Louise and her Uncle Bert, you will want to get a look at them first too. During the cruise try to engage the girl of your dreams in discussions of books or politics if you find yourself with her on the promenade deck in the moonlight, while the band is playing 'I Told Every Little Star'. It won't work, but try it. All this, I suppose, is really no more concern of mine than why you keep fireworks in the house, so I will not pursue it further.

I hope that the foregoing helpful hints for a happy holiday will make your future sea voyages a little easier and merrier and safer. You need not, to be sure, take my advice or follow my example, in every situation and contretemps I have described hereinabove. If you want to put the shoe back on the sick lady's foot, or just leave it where you found it, feel free to do so. The reason I put the shoe on the table with the handbag was – but we have been all through that. I am beginning to repeat myself. Bon Voyage!

An Introduction

LEAFING THROUGH Plutarch's *Lives* on a winter's day, I came upon the story of Xanthippus and his dog. It seems that the old Greek, fleeing Athens one time by ship, left his dog behind – or thought he left him behind. To his amazement and delight, the dog, in the finest whither-thou-goest tradition known to the animal kingdom, plunged into the sea and swam after the galley all the way to Salamis, a feat

of which even a seal might well be proud. When the dog died, Xanthippus built a conspicuous tomb for it, high on a windy cliff, that men, infirm of purpose, weak of heart, might be reminded of the miracle which can be wrought by courage, loyalty, and resolution.

Man first gained superiority over the other animals not because of his mind, but because of his fingers. He could pick up rocks and throw them, and he could wield a club. Later he developed the spear and the bow and arrow. It is my theory that the other animals, realizing they were as good as cooked if they came within range of Man's weapons, decided to make friends with him. He probably tried to make a pet and companion out of each species in turn. (It never occurred to him, in those days, to play or go hunting with Woman, a peculiarity which has persisted down to the present time.)

It did not take Man long – probably not more than a hundred centuries – to discover that all the animals except the dog were impossible around the house.* One has but to spend a few days with an aardvark or a llama, command a water-buffalo to sit up and beg, or try to housebreak a moose, to perceive how wisely Man set about his process of elimination and selection. When the first man brought the first dog to his cave (no doubt over and above his wife's protests), there began an association by which Man has enormously profited. It is conceivable that the primordial male held the female, as mate or mother, in no aspect of

---

* There is no deliberate intention here to offend admirers of the cat, although I don't really much care whether I do or not.

esteem whatsoever, and that the introduction of the dog into the family circle first infected him with that benign disease known as love. Certain it is that the American male of today, in that remarkable period between infancy and adolescence, goes through a phase, arguably atavistic, during which he views mother, sister, and the little girl next door with cold indifference, if not, indeed, outspoken disdain, the while he lavishes whole-hearted affection on Rex or Rover. In his grief over the loss of a dog, a little boy stands for the first time on tiptoe, peering into the rueful morrow of manhood. After this most inconsolable of sorrows there is nothing life can do to him that he will not be able somehow to bear.

If Man has benefited immeasurably by his association with the dog, what, you may ask, has the dog got out of it? His scroll has, of course, been heavily charged with punishments: he has known the muzzle, the leash, and the tether; he has suffered the indignities of the show-bench, the tin can on the tail, the ribbon in the hair; his love life with the other sex of his species has been regulated by the frigid hand of authority, his digestion ruined by the macaroons and marshmallows of doting women. The list of woes could be continued indefinitely. But he has also had his fun, for he has been privileged to live with and study at close range the only creature with reason, the most unreasonable of creatures.

The dog has got more fun out of Man than Man has got out of the dog, for the clearly demonstrable reason that Man is the more laughable of the two animals. The dog has long been bemused by the singular activities and the curious practices of men, cocking his head inquiringly to one side, intently watching and listening to the strangest goings-on in the world. He has seen men sing together and fight one another in the same evening. He has watched them go to bed when it is time to get up, and get up when it is time to go to bed. He has observed them destroying the soil in vast areas, and nurturing it in small patches. He has stood by while men built strong and solid houses for rest and quiet, and then filled them with lights and bells and machinery. His sensitive nose, which can detect what's cooking in the next township, has caught at one and the same time the bewildering smells of the hospital and the munitions factory. He has seen men raise up great cities to heaven and then blow them to hell.

The effect upon the dog of his life with Man is discernible in his eyes, which frequently are capable of a greater range of expression than Man's. The eyes of the sensitive French poodle, for example, can shine with such an unalloyed glee and darken with so profound a gravity as to disconcert the masters of the earth, who have lost the key to many of the simpler magics. Man has practiced for such a long time to mask his feelings and to regiment his emotions that some basic quality of naturalness has gone out of both his gaiety and his solemnity.

The dog is aware of this, I think. You can see it in his eyes sometimes when he lies and looks at you with a long, rueful gaze. He knows that the bare foot of Man has been too long away from the living earth, that he has been too busy with the construction of engines, which are, of all the things on earth, the farthest removed from the shape and intention of nature. I once owned a wise old poodle who used to try to acquaint me with the real facts of living. It was too late, though. I would hastily turn on the radio or run out and take a ride in the car.

The dog has seldom been successful in pulling Man up to its level of sagacity, but Man has frequently dragged the dog down to his. He has instructed it in sloth, pride, and envy; he has made it, in some instances, neurotic; he has even taught it to drink. There once lived in Columbus, Ohio, on Franklin Avenue, a dog named Barge. He was an average kind of dog, medium in size and weight, ordinary in markings. His master and mistress and their two children made up a respectable middle-class family. Some of the young men in the neighborhood, however, pool-shooting,

motor-cycle-riding bravos, lured Barge into a saloon one day and set before him a saucer of beer. He lapped it up and liked it. From there it was but an easy step to whisky.

Barge was terribly funny, the boys thought, when he got stiff. He would bump into things, hiccup, grin foolishly, and even raise his muzzle on high in what passed for 'Sweet Adeline.' Barge's coat became shabby, his gait uncertain, and his eyes misty. He took to staying out in the town all night, raising hell. His duties as watchdog in the home of his owners were completely neglected. One night, when Barge was off on one of his protracted bats, burglars broke in and made off with his mistress's best silver and cut glass.

Barge, staggering home around noon of the next day, sniffed disaster when he was still a block away. His owners were waiting for him grimly on the front porch. They had not straightened up after the burglars. The sideboard drawers were pulled out, the floor littered with napkins and napkin rings. Barge's ears, chops, and tail fell as he was led sternly into the house to behold the result of his wicked way of life. He took one long, sad look around, and the cloudiness cleared from his head. He realized that he was not only a ne'er-do-well but a wrongo. One must guard the house at night, warn the family of fire, pull drowning infants out of the lake. These were the sacred trusts, the inviolable laws. Man had dragged Barge very far down, but there was still a spark of doghood left in him. He ran quickly and quietly upstairs, jumped out of an open window, and killed himself. This is a true and solemn legend of Franklin Avenue.